GREAT EVENTS
IN THE LIFE OF
CHRISTOPHER COLUMBUS

★**5** *First sights land at San Salvador,*
Bahama Islands, October 12, 1492

★**6** *Returns to Spain to announce*
his discovery to the Queen, 1493

★**7** *Discovers Puerto Rico and Jamaica*
on his second voyage, 1493-1496

THE STORY OF
Christopher Columbus

" 'Brave Admiral, say but one good word:
What shall we do when hope is gone?'
The words leapt like a leaping sword:
'Sail on! sail on! sail on! and on!' "

—JOAQUIN MILLER

"And if I refuse?" Columbus asked

THE STORY OF
Christopher Columbus

By NINA BROWN BAKER

Illustrated by DAVID HENDRICKSON

ENID LAMONTE MEADOWCROFT
Supervising Editor

PUBLISHERS Grosset & Dunlap NEW YORK

PRINTED IN THE UNITED STATES OF AMERICA

Library of Congress Catalog Card No. 52-11066

For
KATHERINE LADOF

Contents

Contents

Illustrations

THE STORY OF
Christopher Columbus

"That's what I'd like to be," Christopher said

CHAPTER ONE

"I Am Meant for Better Things!"

IT WAS hot in the little yard behind the weaver's shop. High walls on every side shut out the breeze. A wood fire burned under the huge dye kettle. Two boys with sticks stood over the kettle, stirring and turning the wool yarn. When they had begun their work, the yarn had been dingy gray, just as it came from the sheep. Now it was turning a beautiful bright blue.

"Christopher! Bartholomew! Come at once. Mama wants you."

The brothers looked up as their sister came toward them. Bianca was a tall, pale girl. She was older than the two boys, who were ten and twelve.

[3]

"Look at you!" she scolded. "Splattered with dye from head to foot. Why do you think we use such long sticks? It's so we can keep away from the dye as we stir. But you—Christopher, there is blue dye even in your red hair!"

The older boy laughed cheerfully.

"Maybe I'm tired of having red hair, sister. I'm certainly tired of hearing jokes about it. Blue hair would make a nice change, anyway. Don't you think so, Bartholomew?"

The younger boy looked worried.

"But people don't *have* blue hair, Christopher," he said seriously.

Christopher laughed again.

"People here in Genoa don't have blue hair, you mean. But Genoa isn't the whole world. Very likely there are countries where everyone's hair is blue. Why not? We don't know what it's like in the rest of the world. All we know is this same old Genoa. Some day—"

"Christopher!" His sister spoke sharply. "Did you hear what I said? Mama wants you boys in the house. Here, give me the stick. I'll stir the dye now. Go on. She is waiting."

[4]

The boys went into the shop. It was dim and dark there. The air was heavy with the smell of fresh-dyed wool. From the wooden loom came a noisy clanking. Bales of raw wool were stacked around the walls. The table was covered with rolls of finished cloth.

"You wanted us, Mama?"

When Christopher spoke, the woman at the loom stopped her work. She got up and went to the table. She was a big, strong-looking woman with a loud voice.

"You'll have to deliver this cloth to the tailor," she said briskly. "It was promised for today. Oh, my goodness!" she broke off as a baby's cry came from upstairs.

"Giovanni!" she shouted. "You have wakened your baby brother!"

A smaller boy's head appeared at the top of the steps.

"I didn't wake him, Mama," he said. "I was playing very quietly."

"Well, rock the cradle and put him to sleep again. I can't attend to everything," said the woman.

She turned back to Christopher and Bartholomew.

"This cloth, now. The tailor must have it before nightfall. And your father—" she paused, then went on quickly. "Your father had to go out on business. No doubt he was delayed. We'll have to take care of it ourselves. Can you carry the big rolls? Can you keep them from falling into the mud?"

"Oh, yes, Mama," Christopher answered eagerly. "We know the way. And we'll be very, very careful. Here, Bartholomew. Stretch out your arms and let me load you."

With the mother's help, both boys soon had

[6]

their arms full. These were fine soft woolens, fit for a nobleman. Some were scarlet, some bright orange, some a deep rich purple.

The brothers left the shop and came out into full sunshine. The Italian sky was blue above them. There was a sparkle in the crisp sea air. Christopher sniffed it with delight.

"How I hate the shop!" he said as they walked along. "The smell, the noise! Even the feel of the wool on my fingers. I hate it all! Why should any man choose a weaver's trade?"

His brother looked at him in surprise. "It's our parents' trade, Christopher. It will be ours one day."

"It will never be mine!" Christopher said violently. "I am meant for better things. I feel it—I know it! I—"

He broke off as his brother suddenly pushed him back against a wall. They were walking in an unpaved street. Christopher had not noticed a horseman galloping toward them. He was a young knight, splendid in gleaming armor. A plume waved in his helmet. From his shoulders swung a crimson velvet cloak.

"Whew!" Bartholomew exclaimed, when

the knight had passed. "That was a close call. Another minute, and his horse would have splashed mud all over our cloth. Come on, Christopher. What are you looking at?"

"At him." Christopher's eyes followed the dashing rider. "I'm looking at the nobleman, Bartholomew. That's what I'd like to be. Yes, and I will. When I grow up, I'll be a noble knight."

Bartholomew laughed. "When you grow up, brother, you will be a weaver. Father is a weaver's son. Mother is a weaver's daughter. Their grandparents were weavers. You and I will be weavers, and so will our little brothers. What's wrong with weaving? It's a good trade."

"It's not good enough for me," Christopher answered. "I tell you I am meant for something better. You'll see!"

They walked on, taking their time. It was not often that they had a chance to stroll through the streets. When they could be spared from the shop, they went to the parish school. But work came first, and Mama always found plenty of work for them.

They turned into a busy main street. A tavern stood on a corner, door and windows open to the warm summer air. As the boys passed, they could hear men's voices inside. They seemed to be talking politics.

Bartholomew glanced at his brother. One voice was their father's. Christopher nodded as he met his brother's eye.

"Our father's business delays him for a long time," he said. "No wonder we have to deliver the cloth in his place."

The younger boy looked anxious.

"Christopher," he said, "it is not for us to say what our father should do. But it seems to me he spends too much time in the tavern. Bianca and Mama have to do most of the work."

Christopher laughed. "Our father is no fonder of the weaver's trade than I am. The tavern suits him better. Oh, he is no drunkard. It is not for the wine he goes there. He likes the good fellowship, and the talk, and the company of other men. He would never have chosen to be a weaver. He is one only because his father was."

"And we shall be weavers too, because our

father is." Bartholomew sighed. "Is there no end to this, then? Must the son forever follow in the father's footsteps? I—I don't like weaving very much either, Christopher. But I never thought there was anything to do about it."

"Well, I shall do something about it," Christopher answered. "Our father is a weaver, although he hates it. I will not do what I hate. When I grow up, I will be—"

"You will be a noble knight," Bartholomew laughed. "So you told me. And just how is this going to happen? I'd like to know."

"So would I," Christopher agreed frankly. "Never mind, it will happen. You'll see. And here we are at the tailor's."

They delivered the cloth, and came outside. The sun was sinking now. It was nearly dark when they reached home.

The shop was empty. The loom was silent. A delicious smell floated down the stairway. The boys followed their noses up to the family living room.

The table was set for supper. In the center was a wooden bowl heaped high with purple grapes. Beside it were two smaller bowls. One held olives. The other held cloves of garlic. There were two long loaves of crusty bread.

The family took their places. Bianca came in from the kitchen, carrying a tureen of steaming soup. The father asked a blessing. Then he ladled the soup out into smaller bowls.

"And where have you been so late, my boys?" he asked.

"They delivered the new cloth to the tailor," Mama said sharply. "Since there was no one else to do it!"

"Good, good!" The father was a gentle little man with a friendly smile. He did not seem to

[*11*]

notice at all that his wife was cross with him.

"I meant to deliver the cloth myself," he went on. "But a business matter came up that kept me busy. Please pass the bread, my dear. And let me congratulate you on this delicious soup."

Christopher ate in thoughtful silence. His father was a fine man. A loving husband and a kindly father. But certainly he was a man in the wrong job. Because he did not like his work, he neglected it.

Why should a son always have to follow a father's trade? It was a silly notion. "When my turn comes," Christopher promised himself again, "I shall break away. Whatever happens, I will never be a weaver."

CHAPTER TWO

Aboard the Bonnie Bell

Y OU can go to school today, boys." Mama
sighed as she looked around the empty shop.
"All the raw wool is used up. We can do no
more work until more wool comes from Scotland."

Mama spoke as though this were bad news.
She hated to be idle.

It was not bad news to Christopher and
Bartholomew. For weeks now they had been
too busy to go to school. The classroom would
be a nice change from the dye pot.

For school they dressed in their best. Their
everyday clothes were splashed with dye, and
full of mended holes. But each boy had one
good suit for school and church. They put
them on now.

[*13*]

Christopher drew up his long woolen stockings and tied them to the tail of his shirt. Then he put on his knee-length wool jacket. His stockings and jacket were of undyed wool. Bright colors were forbidden by law to common people. Only the nobles could wear them. Christopher loved the beautiful colors he saw in the shop. How wonderful it would be to be a nobleman, and dress in orange and violet!

"Come on, brother," Bartholomew said. "Don't stand there dreaming. You know how Father Benedict scolds a tardy scholar."

"I'm ready." Christopher caught up his round woolen cap. And the boys set out.

Halfway to the church school they met their father. He had left the house right after breakfast. Now he seemed in a great hurry.

"I was going home to get you, boys," he said. "I have a treat for you. The Scottish ship *Bonnie Bell* is in port. She'll be sure to have wool for us. Who wants to come to the dock with me?"

"I do!" Christopher said quickly. His father knew how he loved to watch the ships.

"You too, Bartholomew?" the father asked.

[*14*]

But the younger boy shook his head. "Thank you, Father. But I'd rather go to school."

A frown crossed the father's merry face. How different his two boys were! Christopher, tall, strong, redheaded, always ready for adventure. And little timid Bartholomew, only interested in books.

"Well," he thought, "we can't all be alike." He turned to Bartholomew. "Get along with you, then," he said. "Make your brother's excuses to Father Benedict."

Bartholomew ran off to school.

Christopher and his father followed a narrow street to the water side. The harbor was crowded with ships great and small. There was a bustle of loading and unloading. Bales of hide for leather were being dumped upon the dock. From a French ship men were rolling great barrels of wine.

Christopher's eyes shone. It always made him excited and happy to come to the docks. The sight of ships gave him a feeling he could not explain. It was as if he belonged among them. And yet he had never set foot upon a deck. It was very strange. His home was a weaver's shop. Why should he feel that he could only be really at home on a ship?

"There's the *Bonnie Bell*," his father said. "Hi, Captain MacGregor!"

The big man on the bridge peered down at them.

"Come aboard, Master Colombo!" he roared.

Christopher followed his father up the gang-plank. He bowed politely when he was introduced to the captain.

"A fine well-grown lad," the captain said. "Well, Master Colombo, I have bad news for you. There was a blight upon Scotch sheep this year. Some queer sickness has struck them down. I've no good wool at all. A few bales of

poor stuff you wouldn't want. I had to fill my hold with flax from Ireland. Could you use that instead?"

Christopher's father shook his head. "No. We don't have wheels for spinning linen thread. And my weaving loom would not take it. Well, this is a disappointment, Captain. We're all out of wool. I'll just have to wait for another ship."

"Don't pin your hopes on another ship," the captain warned. "There's little wool in Scotland this year. I'm sorry for your disappointment. Let's have a bite to eat to cheer you. Come down to my cabin."

Christopher lingered and cleared his throat. "Sir," he said to the captain, "may I look around the ship? I've never been aboard one before."

"Why, certainly," replied the captain. "Run along, lad. You'll find us below when you've seen it all."

Christopher spent a happy hour, exploring the *Bonnie Bell* from stem to stern. Everything he saw delighted him.

The lean, sunburned sailors were a friendly

lot. They answered Christopher's questions cheerfully. Some of the questions seemed very funny to them. But they noticed that the boy never asked the same question twice. He learned very quickly, this young landlubber.

"It wouldn't take many voyages to make a real sailor of you," the boatswain told him.

Presently his father and the captain came on deck again.

"Well, young fellow?" the captain demanded. "What do you think of my ship?"

"I think she's the most wonderful thing in the world!" Christopher exclaimed.

[*19*]

He spoke so eagerly that both men laughed. Christopher felt the captain's keen blue eyes looking him over.

"How would you like to ship aboard her, then?" Captain MacGregor asked abruptly.

"Me?" Christopher could not believe his ears.

"Yes, you. You're a strong, bright boy, and you seem to like the ship. I could use a cabin boy. It would be hard work, mind. You'd look after the cabin, keep it clean and tidy. Make my bed. Serve my meals. And make yourself as useful on deck as you could. Hard work, you see. No time for play."

[*20*]

"Such work would be play for me!" Christopher said joyfully. "Oh, sir, do you really mean it? Father, would you let me go?"

"Why not?" replied his father. "It's what you want. A boy should please himself once in a while. He won't have much chance to do it when he's a man. Yes, if Captain MacGregor will take you, I've no objection."

Plans were quickly made. The *Bonnie Bell* would be in Genoa for a week. When she sailed back to Scotland, Christopher would sail with her.

He walked home at his father's side. He still could not believe this wonderful thing could be true. Then a thought came to him.

"Father," he asked, "what will Mama say? She needs me in the shop. She'll never let me go."

The father smiled. "You forget what Mac-Gregor told us. There's no wool to be had. The shop will be idle. And with you away, there'll be one mouth less to feed. Your mother is a sensible woman. She will not object."

Soon they reached home. Christopher's

mother was waiting for her husband to bring back the new wool. She wrung her hands when he told her there was none.

"What shall we do?" she wailed. "We will all starve!"

"Now, now, wife, we won't starve," the father said. "It's only for a few months, until next year's wool comes in. And I have a little plan to tide us over. What do you say to opening a cheese store? We can get an empty room in the house next door."

"A store?" his wife asked uncertainly. "I don't know. We are weavers. We have never done anything else. How can we keep a store?"

"We can do it," her husband said cheerfully. "Now, about our boy here. Christopher has a chance to go to sea with Captain Mac-Gregor."

The mother's eyes filled with tears. "What is happening to our family? We are not shopkeepers and sailors. We are weavers! Why must we turn ourselves into something else? I won't have it!"

She began to sob. Her husband patted her shoulder.

[22]

"Come, my dear, don't be so unhappy. It is only for a little while. Next year the good Scotch wool will come in again. Christopher will give up the sea. Everything will be as it was before. Now dry your eyes and give the boy your blessing."

The mother looked up.

"Well, so long as it's only for a few months," she said doubtfully. "I've always heard that Captain MacGregor is a good Christian man. He won't abuse the boy, like some shipmasters. Yes, you may try one voyage, Christopher. But mind you behave yourself. Don't learn any rough ways, or any swearwords. I know what sailors are like."

"Oh, I promise you I won't, Mother dear!" Christopher hugged her to him. She was cross and impatient sometimes, poor hard-working Mama. But always she loved her children and wanted to see them happy.

He squeezed her tight. "Thank you, thank you for letting me go!" he cried.

"Go where?" Bartholomew stood in the doorway, his sister beside him. Bianca had been out on an errand. She had met Bartholo-

[*23*]

mew as he was coming home from school.

Excitedly Christopher poured out his news.

His sister shook her head. "They wouldn't get me on a ship. I've heard it rocks about and makes you dreadfully sick."

"Seasickness—what is that?" Christopher laughed scornfully. "It's all over in a day or two. And some people never get it at all. I'm sure I shan't. Well, brother? Aren't you going to congratulate me?"

"Yes, if it's what you want," Bartholomew answered. "I can't see why you want it. If we're not needed in the shop, we can spend all the time at school. I don't see how you can bear to miss school. And to miss it for a ship!"

"Well, go to school if you wish," Christopher laughed. "School is well enough. But to like school better than a ship—no, that I cannot understand!"

"Brothers never understand each other," the mother said briskly. Her tears were dried now. Gently she pushed Christopher aside and began setting the table for supper.

Her mind was busy with new plans. This idea of a store would not be so bad, she thought. Bianca could help her father. It would be easier work for the girl than bending over a loom all day. And the mother herself would have more time to look after the baby.

She smiled at her husband. "We should get the room next door very cheap," she said. "It has been empty a long time. Be sure you drive a good bargain, now. Bianca, we must look over Christopher's clothes. No doubt it's cold at sea. We'll have to make him a good thick cloak. When are you leaving, son?"

"Next week, Mama."

Christopher tried to sound very calm, but his voice shook with excitement. It was true, it was *really* true! By this time next week he would be aboard the *Bonnie Bell*. Even now it was hard to believe it. Oh, this would be a day to remember all his life!

CHAPTER THREE

The Brothers Make a Bargain

IT WAS a year later. Bartholomew sat on the sunny church steps and waited for his brother. Christopher had been a long time with Father Benedict. Was this a good sign, or a bad one?

The younger boy sighed. Things had not been pleasant at home since Christopher had returned from his last voyage.

There was plenty of wool now. And Mama said it was time Christopher gave up the sea. He was needed in the shop. But Christopher had set his heart on being a sailor.

Father would have agreed. But Mama wept and scolded. At last she had said she would let the priest settle it. So Christopher had come to lay it all before Father Benedict. He was in the priest's study now. What would the answer be?

It was very quiet in the church square. Bartholomew picked up a stick and began drawing on the dusty ground. Before he knew it he was making a map. Here was the square,

with the streets leading out of it. Here was the church and school.

He was so busy that he forgot to watch for his brother. Then Christopher came clattering down the church steps. He was smiling.

Bartholomew jumped up. His feet stamped out the map.

"What did he say?" he demanded excitedly. "Is it good news?"

[27]

"Good and bad. He says it's my duty to go back to the shop. I'm only thirteen. I must obey my parents, Father Benedict says."

"Oh, Christopher! Then it *is* bad news! Didn't you tell him how you hate weaving? And how you love the sea? Couldn't he understand that?"

"Father Benedict understands everything," Christopher answered soberly. "I think he is the wisest man in Genoa. He made me see what a fool I'd been."

"A fool?" repeated Bartholomew. "Because you hate weaving? Then I'm another fool. For I hate it, too."

"Come along," Christopher said. "We must go home. I'll tell you the rest on the way. I said there was good news as well as bad."

"Well, tell me the good, then!" Bartholomew exclaimed. "I'm waiting."

They went down the steps and turned into their own street.

"At first Father Benedict was very stern," Christopher began. "That was when he talked about my duty. But after I had promised to go back to the shop—"

"Well? Well? Get on with it, brother!"

Christopher smiled. "He said it would be different when I am grown up. He does not believe a son must always follow his father's trade. He says a man has a right to choose what he shall do. When I'm twenty-one I can be a sailor if I wish. And no one should stop me."

"But it will be too late then!" Bartholomew exclaimed.

"No, it won't. Because I can be learning while I'm growing up. Oh, there's so much to learn, Bartholomew! Things I never thought of. How does a pilot steer by the stars? How does a captain plot his course? There were sixty-year-old men on the *Bonnie Bell* who didn't know those things. A common seaman has no chance to learn them."

"And you don't plan to be a common seaman?"

"Of course I don't!" Christopher answered. "One day I shall be captain of my own ship. And I'll sail where I choose. Not safe little voyages to Scotland and France. That is so dull! I'll go to the faraway countries. Maybe I'll sail right out into the Ocean Sea, where no ship has ever gone. I might get to India, or Cathay—who knows? I might—"

Bartholomew tugged at his arm.

"Come back to earth, Christopher! Never mind what you might do some day. What are you going to do now? What is all this about learning navigation on dry land? It sounds foolish to me."

"But it isn't foolish. It's common sense," Christopher answered earnestly. "Father Benedict explained it all. You see, navigation is a science. It takes in mathematics, and astronomy, and—oh, lots of things. Well, these things are all in books. I can learn them while I'm working in the shop. Father Benedict will lend me the right books."

Bartholomew laughed. "You never spent much time on mathematics at school, Christopher. And you'll have to improve your Latin if you expect to read scientific books."

"I know. I'm counting on you to help me," Christopher answered. "You're the student of the family. Oh, it won't be easy, I know that. But Father Benedict says I can do it. And I will!"

"Father Benedict says I can do it. And I will!"

"And now it's a sea captain you want to be," Bartholomew said. "Last year you told me you meant to be a noble knight when you grow up."

"I shall be both," Christopher answered. "Why not? The admirals in the royal navy are noblemen. Yes, that's what I'll be. Don Christopher Columbus, Admiral of the Ocean Sea! How do you like that for a title?"

Both boys laughed. Yet Bartholomew was not quite sure that his brother was joking. Christopher strode along now, with his head in the air and his eyes filled with dreams.

And what crazy dreams they were, Bartholomew thought. The Ocean Sea, which we now call the Atlantic, stretched away into the unknown. No ship ventured far upon it. Sailors believed there were monsters out there, sea serpents and dragons. Ships in Atlantic waters kept close to the coast. And now Christopher talked boldly of sailing right out into those fearful waves!

"He's a strange boy," Bartholomew thought, as he hurried to keep up with his brother's long strides.

"Christopher," he said timidly, "I want to ask you something. You said Father Benedict doesn't believe a son has to follow his father's trade. He said you could do as you liked when you're a man. Well, what about me?"

"You? What do you mean?"

"I mean I don't want to be a weaver, either. Do I have to? When I'm grown up, I mean?"

"No, of course you don't have to," Christopher answered. "Father Benedict says a man has a right to choose. What do you want to be?"

"A map maker," Bartholomew answered shyly. "I've never told anyone. I thought I must be a weaver, like Father. But if I could choose—I'm very good at making maps, you know. And it's a good trade. Especially in a seaport town like this. A ship can't sail without maps and charts. I know I could earn my living as a map maker."

"Well, then, you shall," Christopher answered heartily. "We'll talk to Father Benedict. He says we're to spend as much time in school as we can. He'll help us both. Now listen, Bartholomew."

[*33*]

They were almost home. Christopher laid a warning hand on his brother's arm.

"Not a word of all this to Mama. She has worried enough. We'll just tell her I promised Father Benedict to go into the shop. For the next few years we'll be good little weavers. But we'll help our young brothers learn the trade. We'll teach them all we know. Then, when we're ready to go, we can easily be spared. Is it a bargain?"

"It's a bargain." Bartholomew clasped his brother's hand. "Oh, Christopher, I'm so glad for both of us. We'll work so hard, and study so hard, that the time will fly. And then we'll begin to live!"

CHAPTER FOUR

"The Time Has Come!"

THE brothers kept their promise. For the next six years they worked hard at the weaving trade. Their mother said she did not know what she would have done without them. She told her neighbors she had the best sons in Genoa.

They were always glad to remember that she said that. For when Christopher was nineteen, the mother died.

A few weeks after the funeral, the father called his sons to him.

"We must talk about the future," he said seriously. "I am thinking of giving up the weaving business. I did better when we had the little cheese store. Perhaps I should open the store again. You boys must help me decide."

Christopher smiled. He was not surprised. His father liked storekeeping. It gave him a chance to chat with his friends who came to buy. His father was a very good storekeeper, too. It was work that suited him.

"I am glad," Christopher said. "But why do you ask us, Father? It's for you to decide."

"No, it is for you." The father's kind face looked distressed. "I can build the store into a nice little business. It will keep me, and your sister, and the little ones. The younger boys can help me. But—but—"

He faltered, and could not go on. Bartholomew looked puzzled. Christopher burst into sudden laughter.

"I know what you're trying to say, Father. That there's no place for Bartholomew and me in your new business. Is that it?"

"I am ashamed to say it," the father answered. "If you boys wish, we will keep on with the weaving. If we don't, what will become of you two?"

Bartholomew also began to laugh. The father looked at them in amazement. The two boys laughed and laughed and could not stop.

"I don't see anything to laugh at," the father said. "It's a sad thing when a father can't take his sons into his business. I have not slept for many nights, worrying about it."

Christopher's face sobered.

"Dear Father," he said affectionately, "you won't need to worry any more. We don't want to be store clerks. We didn't want to be weavers. We kept on with it because it was our duty.

But now—oh, Bartholomew, the time has come. We can tell him our plans now."

Eagerly they poured them out.

Bartholomew would be a map maker. He had learned all that Father Benedict could

[37]

teach him. For several months he had been making ships' charts in his spare time. A shop here in Genoa had bought some of them. He felt sure the shopkeeper would hire him.

The father listened in surprise.

"Did your mother know of this?" he asked.

Bartholomew shook his head. "We meant to wait till we were past twenty," he said. "We dreaded telling her. But Father Benedict said a man has a right to choose."

"Father Benedict knew," Christopher put in. "He said we must do as Mama wished until we were grown. We tried to be good sons to her, Father."

"And you were, my boys. None better. She always said so. Well, well, this is a surprise. How about you, Christopher? Will you work in a map maker's shop too?"

"Not I," Christopher laughed. "The maps show distant countries on paper. I'm going to the countries themselves. Oh, Father, surely you must know my dream. Ever since you took me aboard the *Bonnie Bell*, I've had no other. A sailor's life is the life for me. And now my real life can begin!"

The father blinked. "Then you'll be going to sea, Christopher?"

"As soon as I can find a ship," Christopher answered eagerly. "It will not take long. I'll have to sign on as a common seaman. But I have been studying navigation. I know more than most sailors ever know. Once I'm aboard, I'll find a way to use my studies."

They spent an hour in excited talk. Then the father rose. He was smiling happily.

"It's all settled, then. I'll sell the weaving business and open the store. And you boys will go ahead with your own plans."

They nodded eagerly. The father took a hand of each.

"Remember this, boys. You are still my sons. This is still your home. If you get into difficulties—well, there's always a roof for you here. God bless you, my sons, wherever you go. Your dear mother was right. You are the best sons in Genoa."

Before the week ended, the brothers had left home. Bartholomew went to his friend the map maker. There was no job in the shop, but the map maker had an idea. He gave Bartholomew a letter to his brother in Lisbon, Portugal.

Portugal was a great seagoing nation. The map maker's brother had set up his shop in the capital. He made maps and charts for Portuguese ships. He was so busy that he needed a skilled helper.

So Bartholomew set out for Lisbon. The new job proved a good one. He settled down happily in the Portuguese capital. Six years passed before he and his brother met again.

By that time, Bartholomew had gone into the map-making business for himself. He was at work in his shop one summer afternoon when the door opened. A scarecrow figure, dressed in rags, stood on the threshold. Bartholomew thought the man was a beggar until he spoke.

"Good afternoon, brother. May I come in?" It was Christopher's voice. Bartholomew jumped up.

"Christopher!" he cried. "Is it really you? Come in, come in. I can't believe my eyes!"

"Perhaps you can't believe your nose either." The visitor smiled wearily. "That is fish you smell. Don't come too close. I rode to

the city on a cartload of fish. Could I have a
bath? And some clean clothes?"

"Of course." Bartholomew threw his arms
around his brother. "You were right about the
smell," he laughed. "Never mind. Come upstairs to my rooms. We'll soon clean you up.
Oh, Christopher, it's good to see you again!"

An hour later the brothers faced each other
across the table in the dining room upstairs.
Christopher's filthy rags had been thrown
away. Now, in his brother's Sunday suit, he
stuffed himself with bread and cheese.

At last he leaned back and smiled at his brother.

"You've been very patient, Bartholomew," he said. "But you must be bursting with questions. Go ahead and ask them."

Bartholomew smiled. "I have so many questions that I don't know where to begin," he said. "You must remember that I have had no word of you for years. Your last letter said that you were on a ship, trading up and down the Italian coast. That was a long time ago. And you did not write again."

"I did not write because I had no good news to tell you," Christopher answered. "When we parted, I told you I should soon be a captain and have my own ship. I didn't know how long it would take to do that."

"Father Benedict said books couldn't teach you everything," Bartholomew reminded him.

"I know," Christopher answered. "Books couldn't teach me to reef and steer, to weigh and lower anchor. To learn those things, I had to work as a common seaman. Well, I worked hard. And I kept on studying. At last I became a first mate. Then, on this last voyage, I had my chance to become a captain."

"So you did become a captain at last!" Bartholomew exclaimed.

Christopher smiled sadly. "I was not a captain for long," he said. "My ship, the *Bechalla,* sailed from Greece. We were bound for Lisbon. We knew it would be a dangerous voyage, because of the war with France. But we came safely within sight of the Portuguese coast. I was going to surprise you by a visit from your brother, the captain."

"Yes? Go on," Bartholomew said impatiently. "Did your ship get to Portugal?"

Christopher shook his head. "We were nearing land when trouble came. A fleet of French warships attacked us. Oh, we put up a good fight! But what could we do against their big guns? Cannon balls tore great holes in my brave little ship. She sank at nightfall. So far as I know, all my shipmates were lost."

"May God have mercy on their souls," Bartholomew said soberly. "And thanks be to God that you survived! How did that happen?"

"I'll show you," Christopher answered. He got up and went to the wall. A big map of Portugal hung there. Christopher put his finger on a spot just off the coast.

"A fleet of French warships attacked us"

"Here is where the *Bechalla* went down," he said. "At the last minute I leaped into the sea. I had been wounded. It was not a serious wound, but I was weak from loss of blood. An oar floated past me. I caught it and held on. All night I swam, resting on the oar from time to time. It was the most fearful night of my life."

"I should think so," Bartholomew exclaimed. "But you did come safely to land?"

"Yes, the tide washed me ashore the next morning," Christopher answered. "Here is the place on the map. It is a tiny fishing village. The fishermen took me to their huts and looked after me. When I got better, I asked them the way to Lisbon. They told me I could ride on the next cartload of fish. And here I am."

"Here you are, and most welcome," Bartholomew said warmly. "You have had a bad time, brother, but it is over now. You have come to the right port, Christopher. Portugal is building ships faster than she can find men to sail them. There is a great demand for skilled navigators. I will speak about you to the shipowners who buy my maps. We'll have

[45]

you a new job before Sunday, I promise you."

"As a captain?" Christopher asked.

"I hope so. As an officer, at least." Bartholomew thought a minute. "One of my customers is planning a voyage to Iceland. It is a hard, dangerous passage. Not many ships have gone there. Not many captains want to go again. This customer is having trouble finding a good man to sail his ship. Would you consider it?"

"I'd jump at it!" Christopher said eagerly. "I'm sick of the same old ports. There's no adventure in a safe, easy voyage in seas which are close to home. Iceland, eh? I've never been there. Oh, yes, Bartholomew, that is the job for me. I'll satisfy your friend, never fear. I've learned my trade by hard study and hard work. You can safely recommend me as a captain."

"I'll go and see the shipowner at once," Bartholomew said. "I have no doubt he'll be delighted."

And so it proved. Christopher made a successful voyage to Iceland. From that time on, he was always sure of a post on Portuguese ships. Like his brother, he came to look upon Lisbon as his home.

CHAPTER FIVE

Felipa

WHENEVER he was ashore in Lisbon, on a Sunday, Columbus attended services at the Church of the Two Saints. There he noticed a lovely young girl, named Felipa Perestrello. Sunday after Sunday he knelt where he could watch her beautiful face. Soon he was deeply in love with her. He told his brother Bartholomew that his dearest desire was to win Felipa for his wife.

"The Perestrellos are a noble family," Bartholomew warned him. "They may not think you are good enough for their daughter. Still, the father is dead, and I have heard he did not leave much money. Perhaps the mother would not refuse you her daughter's hand. You can ask, anyway."

"You must come with me," Christopher

[*47*]

said. "I am an unknown sea captain. But you are a respectable businessman of Lisbon. You can speak for me. Tell the mother I am hard-working and serious."

Bartholomew laughed. "Can I truly tell her that? Is it serious to spend all your spare time dreaming of a sea route to India? Some people would not think so."

"And why not?" Christopher demanded. "Portugal could grow rich on trade with India. If only we could find a way to get there! We can't go by land because the Russians and the Turks guard the roads which run through their countries. They wish to keep the Indian trade to themselves. So our merchants are forced to buy silks and pearls from them, instead of buying them in India. But if we could reach India by sea—"

"If, if!" Bartholomew repeated. "Well, let's not talk about India now. It's your wedding we are discussing. Do you think the girl would have you, if her mother consents?"

"She smiles at me from behind her prayer book," Christopher said. "I think that's a good sign, don't you?"

[48]

"We'll soon know," Bartholomew answered. "You must write to the mother and ask if we can call on her. Do it now."

A few days later the permission came. The two brothers dressed in their best, and went to the Perestrello house. Felipa's mother asked many questions and seemed pleased with the answers. At last she agreed that Christopher might marry her daughter.

Then Felipa was called in. She blushed when she saw Christopher, and admitted that she had smiled at the handsome young man in church. She was sure she could be happy as his wife.

They were married in the spring. Columbus bought a comfortable little house. There, a year later, his son Diego was born.

It seemed to Bartholomew that his brother ought to be contented now. He had a good home, a beautiful wife, and a fine baby son. He also had steady work on Portuguese ships.

But Felipa was as extravagant as she was beautiful. She spent her husband's pay as fast as he earned it. Often she pouted because it was not more.

They were married in the spring

Bartholomew spoke about this to his brother one day.

"Felipa has been complaining to me," he said. "She says you are lazy. You refused to make a voyage to England, though it would have brought you much money. Instead you spent all this month reading in the royal library. Your wife doesn't like that."

"My wife doesn't understand," Christopher answered. "No one understands what I'm trying to do. Not even you, my brother. To reach India by sea—that is my hope. I shall never give it up!"

"But it is such a foolish hope," Bartholomew said gently. "I can show you why on the map, Christopher. India lies east of us. But if we sail east, we find the continent of Africa in the way. You can't sail across dry land. And there is no other way."

"You think not?" Christopher's voice grew excited. "Well, let me tell you something. I have read and studied and figured and thought. Yes, and prayed! It has not been in vain. For the answer has come to me. There *is* a way to reach India by sea. And I, I alone, know how it can be done!"

Bartholomew looked so amazed that Christopher laughed.

"No, I have not gone mad," he said. "Look, I'll explain it to you. It's really quite simple. We can reach India, not by sailing east, but by sailing *west!*"

Bartholomew shook his head. This did

sound like madness. To the west was the Atlantic Ocean, which they called the Ocean Sea. And India, as everyone knew very well, lay to the east.

"Don't you see?" Christopher went on earnestly. "The earth is a round globe. You'll agree to that, won't you?"

Bartholomew nodded. "Yes, I agree with the scholars who believe the earth is round. Although I know that many learned men do not think it can be true. But suppose it is so, why—oh, wait! I think I see what you mean."

"Of course you do," Christopher answered. "If the earth is a globe, the path around it is a circle. West leads to east if you follow the circle. So a voyage across the Ocean Sea would bring me to India in time. It would have to do that."

"Well, it's an exciting notion, anyway," Bartholomew said. "But what good is it?"

"Can't you see?" Christopher asked impatiently. "All I need are a few ships and the King's permission to sail them across the ocean. Then I'll go to India and bring back a cargo of Indian goods. After that, Portugal and India can trade with each other. It will make Portugal the richest nation in Europe."

Bartholomew smiled. "Will it make you the richest captain? Felipa will like that."

Christopher sighed. "You don't take me seriously, Bartholomew. No one does. But now that I know how to get to India, I'm going to manage it some way. The first thing I must do is to interest the King of Portugal. How do I go about that?"

"It won't be easy," Bartholomew said. "You don't walk up to a king's palace and knock on his door. You have to know some of the nobles at court. You tell them why you want to see the King. Then, if they think your business is worth while, they make an appointment for you. That is how it's done."

"That's how I shall do it, then," Christopher answered. "Give me a list of these nobles. I'll see as many as I can before I go to sea again."

Columbus spent the next few years trying to reach the Portuguese King. He met some important men of the court. Some of them laughed at him. A few encouraged him. "Come back in a month," they told him. And when the month was up, "Come back in a year." Months and years went by, and still he could not get to the King.

His wife Felipa lost all patience with him. Even his brother grew tired of hearing him talk about his scheme. Only Diego, his little son, was always willing to listen.

Diego and his father took long walks together. "Tell me about India," the little boy would beg. And Columbus would repeat all the strange tales he had read about India. He had read them in a book which had been written many years earlier by a man named Marco Polo.

Marco Polo was an Italian who had journeyed to the East through Turkey. He had lived for a long time in India. He had also lived in Cathay and Cipango—those countries which we now call China and Japan. On his return to Italy he had written an account of all the wonderful things he had seen in these countries.

"Some people say Polo's stories aren't true," Columbus told his son. "They say there couldn't be such a beast as an elephant, or palaces made of solid gold. But I don't see why not. Anyway, I'll know more about India when I see it myself."

"And you will see it, Papa," the little boy said eagerly. "Mama says you'll never get there. But I know better. As soon as the King hears about you, he'll give you the ships so you can go. It won't be long, Papa."

The child's faith was a comfort to his father. And Columbus needed comfort. Time dragged on, and things got no better. They grew worse still when Felipa fell ill. She died after a week's sickness. More trouble followed soon after her death.

CHAPTER SIX

The King's Map

BARTHOLOMEW'S old housekeeper opened the door and peered out into the night. Surely she had heard a knock? But she could see no one. Grumbling, she was turning away. Then a whisper came out of the darkness.

"Caterina! Put out the light. No one must see me enter. Is my brother home?"

"Oh, it's you, Master Christopher," the housekeeper said with relief. "Yes, the master is in."

Caterina blew out her candle. Only then a dark figure slipped through the doorway. Christopher Columbus was wrapped from head to foot in a black cloak. He carried a large bundle in his arms.

He shut the door softly behind him. His

[57]

breath came heavily, as though he had been running. "They mustn't see me here," he gasped.

"No one can see you now," the old woman said. "Go on into the master's room. The curtains are drawn there. Mercy on us, what's this in your arms? If it isn't the little Diego, poor motherless lamb!"

"Look after him, Caterina." Christopher was getting his breath back now. He pulled off the shawls and set Diego on his feet. "There, little man, we're safe in Uncle's house. Go with good Caterina. She'll give you a cake."

Columbus went along the passage to his

brother's study. The hour was late, but Bartholomew was reading in his armchair. He looked up in astonishment.

"Christopher!" he exclaimed. "What brings you here? Is anything wrong?"

"Everything is wrong," Christopher answered grimly. "I am a hunted man, brother. Even now the King's men are battering at my door. I snatched the child from his bed and crawled out through the cellar window. Oh, I knew this trouble was coming. A friendly soldier told me this morning that the King's men were going to arrest me. But I did not expect they would come before tomorrow."

"But why, Christopher, why? What have you done?" Bartholomew asked anxiously.

Christopher dropped into a chair. He looked worried and ill.

"It's a long story, Bartholomew. You know most of it. You know how hard I have tried to reach the King with my plan for India. You know how I have failed. Well, I believe I know now why I have failed. I think these Portuguese nobles do not want me to succeed. To reach the East by sailing west—oh, it is a fine idea! Why should a poor Italian have credit for thinking of it? Why shouldn't they tell the King that the idea is their own?"

"But that is wicked!" Bartholomew exclaimed. "The idea is yours, Christopher. They can't steal it like this."

"Can't they?" Christopher smiled bitterly. "How can I stop them if I'm in jail?"

"But why should you be in jail?" Bartholomew demanded. "You've done nothing wrong."

"The nobles say I have," Christopher answered. "They accuse me of stealing the Toscanelli map. You have heard of it?"

"Oh, yes," Bartholomew answered. "It was made by a famous Italian scholar. He put in all the Eastern lands, just as Marco Polo described them. Dr. Toscanelli sent the map to the King of Portugal. Of course, no one but His Majesty has seen it."

"You may see it now." Columbus took a rolled parchment from under his cloak. "Here it is."

"Christopher! You stole the King's map!"

Columbus smiled bitterly. "You see? Even

my own brother would believe it. When the map is found on me, no one will doubt that I am a thief. Oh, my enemies have worked it out very cleverly."

"But why did you do it?" There were tears in Bartholomew's eyes.

"I am no thief, brother," Christopher answered proudly. "This map is a copy. I wrote to Dr. Toscanelli and asked for it. He sent it to me himself."

Bartholomew drew a long breath. "Well, that's better. Then what have you to fear? Dr. Toscanelli can prove that you are innocent."

"Yes. But how long will it take? They can keep me in jail for months before they bring me to trial. In those months an expedition can sail to India without me. No, I will not stay here to be arrested. I must leave Portugal at once."

"Have you made any plans?" Bartholomew asked.

Columbus nodded. "I have been busy since the soldier told me I was to be arrested," he said. "I sold my house to a neighbor. I can get to Spain on a fishing boat. From Spain I'll make my way to France. Perhaps I'll have better luck with the French King."

"Yes, you are wise to go," Bartholomew agreed. "You'll leave the child with me, of course? Caterina will take good care of him."

"No, Bartholomew," replied Columbus. "I will not leave my son behind."

"Well, you know best," Bartholomew answered. "How can I help you? Do you need money?"

"I need nothing, thank you." Christopher rose and wrapped his cloak around him. "Caterina!" he called. "Bring the boy now."

Little Diego came in munching a piece of cake.

"Are you going to carry me again, Papa?" he asked. "I'm not a baby, you know. I can walk perfectly well. Although of course I can't run as fast as you did."

"You shall walk this time," his father promised him. "But you must walk softly, and not talk at all. We have not far to go. Only down to the fishermen's dock."

"Can you find a boat going out tonight?" Bartholomew asked.

"I will try. If we have to wait, some of the

fishermen will hide us in their warehouse. I have good friends among the fishermen." Christopher held out his hand. "Good-by, brother. God bless you."

"And may God bless you, Christopher," Bartholomew answered warmly. "And you, little nephew." He kissed the child and turned again to his brother. "May He lead you safely to your journey's end."

Christopher smiled with a spark of his old gaiety.

"My journey will end in India," he said. He stowed the rolled map beneath his cloak. "When I come home, Bartholomew, I'll bring my notes to you. You shall make the first map of India as it really is!"

CHAPTER SEVEN

"I Must Go A-Begging!"

THE hillside path was long and steep. Sharp stones hurt little Diego's feet. He was hot, and tired, and very hungry.

Diego was only five, but he was a brave boy. Papa said so. Mama had gone away to heaven. Home was far behind them. They had spent a week on a fishing boat. The boat had no beds. Diego had slept on the deck's bare boards. He had been fearfully seasick. Now they were in this strange land called Spain.

Diego did not understand why these things should be. But he had not complained. He hardly ever cried. That was being brave. Diego wondered how long he could go on being brave. He was so tired!

He looked up into his father's face.

[*65*]

"Will we come to an inn soon?" he asked hopefully. "I saw a nice one in the town down there. We could have stopped at it, Papa."

Columbus tried to smile. He did not want to worry the little boy with grown-up troubles.

There was no money for an inn. The price of his house had gone to pay his wife's bills. Christopher had been too proud to take money from his brother. He hoped that he might soon find work in this Spanish port.

"Courage, little son," he said. "Do you see that big house high above us? It is La Rábida

(Spanish names are easy. The accent mark (′) just means you should accent the word on that syllable. Like this: Rábida—RA-bida.)

monastery. The good monks are always kind to strangers. We shall have food there, Diego. And a bed for the night."

"A real bed?" The little boy began to walk faster.

Soon they came to the monastery gate. An old porter swung it open.

"Enter, brothers. Rest and pray," he said.

Near the gate was an outdoor shrine. Columbus led Diego toward it. "We have come far. The child is hungry," he whispered to the porter. The old man nodded and hurried away.

Father and son knelt before the shrine. The

[67]

gentle face of Our Lady looked sweetly down upon them. A cool breeze swept their cheeks. Diego was smiling as he rose.

"I like this place, Papa," he said. "It is a good place. Will they let us stay here?"

"We'll see."

The porter came back, carrying a tray. On it was a loaf of brown bread and a big chunk of cheese. There was fresh cold milk for the father and for the boy. Little Diego began to stuff himself. Never had food tasted so good!

Columbus sipped his milk. He was too tired and worried to eat. He looked downhill at the town of Palos, and the blue sea of the harbor. There were ships there. Perhaps he might be able to sail on one of them to France.

He started at the sound of footsteps on the gravel. A brown-robed monk called Father Antonio stood before him.

"Who are you, my son?" Father Antonio asked kindly. "And why do you come to La Rábida?"

Columbus sprang to his feet and bowed.

"I am a seaman from Genoa, Father," he answered. "As to why I come—" he gave a bit-

ter laugh. "No king will accept the kingdoms
I offer. So I must go a-begging."

The strange answer interested Father Antonio. He sat down on the bench, taking Diego
on his knee. "Tell me your story," he urged.

So Columbus began.

The monk was astonished when he heard
the story.

"So you plan to reach the East by sailing
west!" he exclaimed. "That is too deep for
me. You must tell our Prior about this. He is
a very learned man, and perhaps he will understand you."

Father Antonio rose. "The porter will find

you a room for the night, Master Columbus. In the morning I will take you to the Prior."

Columbus met the Prior the next day. Father Juan Pérez was a great man in Spain. He had served Queen Isabella as her household chaplain. Her Majesty respected and admired him.

Father Pérez listened to Columbus with interest. The plan of reaching the East by sailing west seemed reasonable to him. He wondered why it had not seemed reasonable to the Portuguese King.

"I wonder, too," Columbus said. "I don't think the King ever heard of it. He is surrounded by men who tell him what they choose. It did not suit them to bring my scheme before him. Well, maybe I'll have better luck at the French court."

"You go next to the King of France, then?"

Columbus nodded. "As soon as I find a ship on which to work my passage," he replied. "I have no money."

"Have you ever thought of laying your plan before our Spanish King and Queen?" Father Pérez asked.

"That would be hopeless," Columbus answered. "I know some merchants in France. They may help me. But there is no one to speak for me at the Spanish court."

Father Pérez smiled. "You are mistaken, Master Columbus. I will speak for you. I believe in you. You must not leave Spain without trying your luck here."

A few days later Columbus made ready to set off for the Court of Spain. He had letters to the Queen and to several of her nobles. Father Pérez had also given him a little gray donkey to ride.

The good monks had offered to keep little Diego while he was gone. The boy was very happy at the monastery. Cheerfully he waved good-by to his father, when Columbus rode away.

One day, a year later, Diego was working in the garden. He saw his father riding the gray donkey up the long hill. The boy dropped his rake and ran to meet him.

Columbus looked tired and worn. There was a streak of gray in his red hair now.

"Did you see the Queen, Papa?" Diego de-

Father Pérez had given him a little gray donkey to ride

manded. "Is she as beautiful as they say? Don't you think I've grown? I'm the gardener's helper now, Papa. Will you come and see my lettuce bed?"

Columbus laughed and hugged him tight.

"Still the same chatterbox, I see. I'll answer all your questions later. Do you know where Father Pérez is?"

"There he comes now," Diego answered. "I'll take the donkey to the stable. Oh, Father Pérez! Papa has come back!"

"So I see." The Prior came up with warm greetings. The two men sat down on the bench near the shrine.

"Tell me about your journey," Father Pérez said. "Did you see the Queen at last?"

"Yes, and she was most kind," Columbus replied. "She says she would like to have a Spanish ship reach India. She wants to send missionaries there to teach the people about Christianity. That was Her Majesty's first thought."

"And a very proper one," the priest agreed. "Will she give you the ships you need?"

"Not yet, Father," Columbus replied. "She

[73]

does not understand how my scheme could work. She wants me to tell my story to the scholars at the University of Salamanca. If they agree that I can really reach India by sailing west, the Queen will aid me. She has promised."

"And Queen Isabella keeps her promises. This is wonderful news, my son," the Prior exclaimed. "You must be overcome with joy."

"Perhaps I should be," Columbus answered. "But—I scarcely dare to hope. I have waited so long. I have tried so hard. What if the scholars decide that my scheme is not a good one? What—oh, there you are, Diego. Did you take care of the little donkey?"

"I gave him his supper." Diego threw himself into his father's arms. "And now tell me all about it, Papa. Did you really see the Queen? Was she wearing her crown? Tell me, tell me—"

Columbus and Father Pérez laughed as the questions tumbled out. The child had grown plump and rosy in his father's absence. The life at La Rábida suited him. He was the pet of all the monks. The monastery was now his home, where he could live safely and happily while his father roved the world.

Columbus spent a pleasant, restful week at La Rábida. Then he mounted his little donkey again and rode off to Salamanca.

CHAPTER EIGHT

The Wise Men of Salamanca

THE great hall of the university was dim. Candles burned on a table at the far end. Thirty men sat around the table. They were the greatest scholars in all Spain.

Most of them wore the robes of priests or monks. Their chairman was a bishop named Hernando de Talavera. The Bishop was speaking as Columbus came in.

"And who is this Christopher Columbus?" The harsh voice thundered out of the shadows. "He is no Spaniard. He claims he was born in Genoa. He admits he ran away from Portugal. Who knows what mischief he made there? What mischief will he make here?"

Columbus had reached the table now. A friendly monk called Brother Diego touched his arm.

"You are Columbus?" he whispered. Christopher nodded. Brother Diego raised his voice.

"Master Columbus is here, brother chairman. He can answer our questions. But first we should let him state his plan."

"That is not necessary," the Bishop said curtly. "The Queen's letter told us all about his plan. She has appointed us to judge it. Brother Francisco, you are the oldest scholar present. Will you ask the first question?"

A very old priest rose stiffly to his feet. He turned his fierce little eyes upon Columbus.

"I understand you claim the earth is shaped like a globe. Is that true?"

Columbus bowed. "My plan rests upon that fact, sir."

"Aha! I thought so. Then tell me this. Are you a Christian? Do you believe in our Holy Bible?"

Columbus looked startled. What had religion to do with this? But he answered politely.

"I am indeed a Christian, sir. And certainly I believe in the Bible."

"Very well." Brother Francisco snatched a Bible from the table. He held it out.

"Show me!" he commanded. "Here, where it tells us how the Lord God created heaven and earth. Where does it say He created the earth a globe? Show me the passage, Master Columbus."

Columbus hesitated. Then he answered frankly.

"I cannot show you that, reverend sir. The Bible does not say the earth was created a globe. But—neither does it say the earth was created flat."

A little murmur went around the table. There was a smile or two. The scientists at the table believed that the earth is round. But all the men there were not scientists. Many of

them refused to believe anything that they could not find in the Bible.

Another old man rose to his feet.

"The idea is ridiculous," he said peevishly. "How could men walk on the other side of a globe? They would have to stand on their heads. The trees would grow with roots in air. The rain and snow would fall upward. Do you expect us to believe such nonsense, young man?"

There was laughter and applause. Columbus stood tall and straight, waiting. Then he spoke in a quiet, respectful voice.

"Sirs, I do not know how men walk on the other side of the earth. I do not know how the trees grow, or how the rain falls. I do not pretend to know. My one hope in life is to go there and find out. When I know, be sure that I will return and tell you."

There was more laughter. This time some of it sounded friendly. But Bishop de Talavera's frown deepened. He did not believe Columbus really wanted to find India. He thought this was all a clever scheme to get money from the Queen. The Bishop meant to see that Her Majesty was not cheated.

Someone spoke from the end of the table.

"Master Columbus, you joke with us. But we are serious men. You say men can live on the other side of a round globe. Then you must explain yourself. How can such a thing be?"

Columbus answered the question with another.

"May I have an egg, please?"

Brother Diego spoke to a servant. There was an uneasy pause. Then an egg was brought in and placed on the table.

Columbus picked it up.

"Gentlemen," he said, "tell me how to make this egg stand on end."

"What childishness is this?" old Brother Francisco fumed. "No one can make an egg stand on end. Its shape forbids it."

Columbus smiled. Very gently he bumped the egg down on the table. The end cracked as it touched the wood. The shell flattened a little. The egg stood there, perfectly balanced on the larger end.

Columbus spoke earnestly.

"Sirs, you did not understand how an egg could stand on end. So you thought it was impossible. Many things seem impossible until we understand them. So it is with the men on the other side of the earth. You think it is impossible for them to live there. But when we understand how they do it, we will see it is not impossible."

He waited a minute, but no one spoke.

"That is my answer," he went on. "I will go and see how men live on the other side. There is some explanation. No doubt it is as simple as this business of the egg. I will bring the explanation back to you."

The Bishop rapped angrily on the table.

"Enough! We did not come here to watch a magician's tricks. That will be all for today. You may return tomorrow, Master Columbus."

The meeting broke up. Columbus turned to the door. Brother Diego caught up with him.

"You did very well, Master Columbus," he said kindly.

"Do you think so, sir? I feel discouraged. I had so much to say. I wanted to talk about the Eastern lands. Instead I had to answer silly questions. Does the Bible say the earth is round? Can men walk on their heads? Really, I expected better things of Spain's great scholars."

His tone was scornful. Brother Diego shook his head to warn him that he must be careful of what he said.

No one else stopped to speak to Columbus. The scholars were hurrying home. The

Bishop had disappeared. A servant was snuffing out the candles.

"Don't judge us all by what you heard today," the friendly friar said, as he and Columbus left the hall. "You will have another chance to discuss your plan with us. And now good night to you, Master Columbus."

Every day for weeks Columbus went back to the university. He answered hundreds of questions. Some of them were foolish. Some were sensible.

At last the Bishop told him he need not come again. He said that the scholars had heard enough. They were ready to write a report to Queen Isabella, telling what they thought of Columbus's plan.

But it was nearly four years before this report went to the Queen. And then the scholars wrote that they had decided against Columbus. They advised that he should not be allowed to make the voyage.

In spite of this report Her Majesty wrote Columbus a very kind letter. She said that she was still interested in his plan. But she reminded him that Spain was now at war with the Moors. She told him that when the war ended she would talk to him again.

The war dragged on for two more years. Columbus made several trading voyages. He always came back to the monastery, for that was now his home.

Then one day he came home to find Diego waiting at the gate.

"The Queen's messenger came while you were away, Papa," he said eagerly. "Here is a letter for you. And here is something else. It's a purse full of gold pieces. The Queen sent them with her letter."

Quickly Columbus tore the letter open. Yes, it was the good news for which he had waited so long!

Queen Isabella wrote that the Moorish war was ending at last. She and the King would

have time to think of other things now. Columbus was to come to court and discuss his plan for reaching India.

He read the letter over and over. Presently Diego tugged at his sleeve.

"The gold, Papa!" the boy said. "You haven't even looked at the gold yet!"

"The gold—oh, yes, the gold," Columbus

[*85*]

answered happily. "Her Majesty sends it so that I may buy a good horse and proper clothing to wear to court. Tomorrow we'll go to the tailor's, Diego."

The next day Diego helped Columbus choose the finest clothing he had ever seen. There were long violet hose, short purple trunks laced with yellow, and a yellow satin doublet. Over it all went a plum-colored robe with a rich fur border.

Everyone in the monastery gathered at the gate to watch Columbus set off for the court. How splendid he looked in his fine new clothes! His son was very proud of him.

"If I didn't know better, I'd think you were a knight," the boy said. He stroked the horse's satiny coat. "I'm sure none of the Queen's knights are so handsome, Papa."

Columbus laughed. "You'd like to have a knight for a father, my boy? Well, who knows? It may happen yet."

CHAPTER NINE

"Take These Jewels!"

THIS way, if you please, sir." The guide halted at the throne-room door. The soldier guards saluted and stepped aside. Head held high, Master Christopher Columbus strode into the great chamber with its high gold ceiling.

On a raised platform at the far end, King Ferdinand and Queen Isabella sat on golden thrones. Men-at-arms with gleaming pikes lined the walls. Gentlemen and ladies in waiting stood respectfully in the background. Candlelight blazed down on silks and velvets and flashing jewels.

Columbus moved toward the thrones. His eyes were dazzled by the splendid spectacle. He felt thankful that he need not appear here in his old shabby clothing.

He came to the platform where the Queen sat. She was very lovely. A jeweled crown rested on her high-piled black hair. An emerald necklace encircled her white throat. Her gown of crimson silk was stiff with embroidery of pearls and gold thread. She smiled as Columbus knelt to kiss her hand.

"Welcome, Master Columbus," she said. "I would present you to my lord King Ferdinand."

The King nodded indifferently. His Majesty did not take much interest in peacetime matters. He was a military leader, and a very good one. For years he had been trying to drive the Moors out of Spain. Now he had succeeded. There were no more battles to interest him. He found court life very dull.

"I would also present Master Columbus," the Queen went on, "to the lord Archbishop."

Columbus started. He had noticed a black shadow between the two thrones. Now he saw that it was no shadow. A black-robed man stood there. He was the newly appointed Archbishop of Granada. Columbus had known him as Talavera, the Salamanca council chairman.

"Master Columbus is no stranger to me, my lady," the Archbishop said. "Six years ago I went fully into his plan. I found that it was not a good one."

King Ferdinand looked surprised. This was all new to him. He had been busy fighting a war. Everything else had been left to the Queen.

Isabella spoke calmly.

"Six years is a long time, reverend Father. A plan which did not seem good then may seem good now. Master Columbus, you may repeat your story. I want the King to hear it."

Talavera moved impatiently.

"It will be a long speech," he said. "I doubt if Your Majesties will find it worth sitting through."

Queen Isabella gave Columbus a kindly smile.

"Be as brief as you can, please."

Columbus bowed. His speech before the throne was brief indeed. He told of the voyages he had made. This was to prove that he was an experienced sailor. Then he set out his theory. The earth was round. Therefore any path around it was a circle. Therefore one could reach the East by sailing west.

The King stopped him then. "One minute, **sir.** I am a plain soldier. I don't pretend to un-

derstand such things. What do you say, my
lord Archbishop? You are a learned man. Does
this idea make sense to you?"

Columbus held his breath. His fate would
hang upon the answer.

"The theory is sound enough," Talavera said sourly.

With a lighter heart Columbus hurried on.

"And so," he said, "I shall come to India. But not India alone. There are other great kingdoms in the East—Cathay and Cipango. Strange and rich lands these kingdoms are. Pearls lie like pebbles on their beaches. The humblest peasant goes wrapped in royal silks. The kings ride upon great beasts called elephants. The palaces are roofed and walled in solid gold."

"How do you know all this?" Ferdinand interrupted.

"I read it in a book, Your Majesty. A book by Marco Polo. This man reached the East through Turkey, a hundred years ago. He lived a long time at the court of the Great Khan. When he came home, he wrote a wonderful book, describing all that he had seen."

Again Ferdinand turned to the Archbishop. This time Talavera laughed scornfully.

"Lies, Your Majesty. All barefaced lies. Marco Polo never left Europe. He wrote the book out of his own head."

Columbus flushed. But the Queen spoke mildly.

"There are scholars who do not think that Marco Polo lied, my lord. But does it matter? There *is* such a land as India. It is a rich land. The Turks go there. This gown I wear is Indian silk, bought in Turkey. It would be better if we could buy our silks in India, and bring them home in Spanish ships. Master Columbus says he can do that. We have only one thing to decide. Shall we let him try?"

King Ferdinand smiled. What a mind she had, this pretty wife of his! The war with the Moors had been costly. Spain needed money. Trade with India would make the country wealthy. Columbus's scheme began to sound very attractive.

"You seem sure of success, Master Columbus," the King said. "Suppose we agree. What reward do you expect for your services?"

Columbus threw back his shoulders.

"First," he said firmly, "I am to be made a nobleman. My title would be Admiral of the Ocean Sea. Second, I am to be made governor of any country I may discover or conquer.

[*93*]

Third, I wish to keep for myself one-tenth of the treasure I bring back."

A gasp went up from the company. Talavera laughed aloud.

"The man is mad!" he exclaimed. "Your Majesties, you see the sort of rascal he is. Now you know why I warned you against him."

King Ferdinand frowned. "I must say, Master Columbus, you set a high price upon your services."

"And they are worth it!" Columbus flashed back. "Think, Sire. I go to these lands in Your Majesty's name. Could a common man represent you? No. It must be done by a nobleman. As for my tenth share of the treasure—think what that treasure will be! Wealth beyond your wildest dreams. Would you grudge me my small share? You risk a little money. I risk my life."

The King still frowned. Isabella spoke to him quickly.

"My lord, we must consider this. Certainly Master Columbus asks a heavy reward. But the reward is only for success. If he fails, he asks nothing. No titles, no wealth. Nothing at all."

"Well, that is reasonable," the King said. "But Spain is poor after this long war. Can we afford the money for such an expedition?"

"*I* can afford it, if Spain cannot!" Isabella exclaimed. She unclasped her emerald necklace. She stripped the rings from her fingers. The heap of jewels lay winking in the candle-light. She beckoned to the royal treasurer.

"These trinkets belong to me, not to Spain," she said proudly. "Santangel, take these jewels and pawn them. They will bring enough to buy Master Columbus his ships."

The royal treasurer bowed. His family was the wealthiest one in all Spain. Gently he pushed the gems toward the Queen.

"It will not be necessary to pawn your jewels, Your Majesty," he said. "I will gladly raise the money Master Columbus needs, if you will give him your permission to go. Do I understand that Your Majesties agree to his conditions?"

Isabella glanced at the King, who nodded.

"It's a good bargain for us," Ferdinand said. "We have nothing to lose, and everything to gain. Yes, certainly I agree."

[95]

"And I!" the Queen said happily.

Santangel bowed. "Then I will arrange everything," he said.

In the shadows behind the throne, Talavera's dark face was like a thundercloud. Columbus did not see it. He saw nothing but the beauty of Isabella's smile as he knelt before her. He heard nothing but her sweet voice as she bade him rise.

"You are a brave man, Master Columbus. I shall pray for your success, and for your safe return. Farewell. May God go with you."

CHAPTER TEN

Columbus Finds a Captain

COLUMBUS went back to Palos. He thought everything would be easy for him now. But at the end of a week he was in despair. He dragged himself wearily up the long hill to La Rábida. When Diego ran to him he motioned him away. The boy hurried off to find Father Pérez.

"I think Papa is sick," Diego said. "He's sitting out there on the bench, staring at the sea. He didn't want to talk to me. What's wrong with him, Father?"

"Nothing, nothing," the priest said. "Go and pick the salad for supper, Diego. Your papa will feel better after he has eaten."

Father Pérez made his way to the bench.

"The boy is worried about you, Christopher," he said. "Are you ill?"

Columbus made room for Father Pérez to sit beside him. "Not ill, Father. Only discouraged. I can't understand it! Palos harbor is full of ships. But I cannot rent any of them. The owners of the boats make a thousand excuses. They say their ships are laid up for repairs. Or that they are already engaged by someone else. Money does not tempt these men. One after the other, they refuse me. Why should this be?"

"I don't know their reasons, but I can guess," the priest answered. "Your expedition is a risky one. You plan to sail out into the

Ocean Sea, where no ship has ever gone. How do the owners know that you will come safely back? They are afraid they would never see their ships again."

"The cowards!" Columbus said angrily. "How is one to deal with such people?"

"It is hard," Father Pérez agreed. "And harder still because you are a stranger to them. You and I know that you are an experienced captain. But you have never sailed from Palos. Those shipowners don't know what you can do. It would be better if one of their own captains tried to rent the ships for you. They might trust him."

"Very well," Columbus answered. "I'll go to one of their own captains. Which one would be best?"

Father Pérez thought a minute. "The Pinzón brothers have made many dangerous voyages. They always come home safely with a good cargo. The oldest one, Martín Alonso, goes all the way to Africa. The Pinzóns are afraid of nothing. Why don't you talk to Martín Alonso? He may be able to help you."

"I'll see him tomorrow." Columbus rose.

[*99*]

"Thank you, Father. You always find a way to make things better for me. Now I'll go and help my gardener son. I'm afraid I was a little cross with him just now. I'll make up to him by letting him put me to work."

Smiling, he strode off toward the garden. Soon Father Pérez could hear him laughing and joking with Diego.

Columbus saw Martín Pinzón the next day. The captain was a big man, red-faced and hearty. He had made a great deal of money trading in distant ports. He was interested in any plan for making more.

"I've traded for Indian silk in Turkey," he said. "It made me a fine profit. Of course the Turks charged me twenty times what the silk must have cost them when they bought it in India. Yes, it would be a great thing to deal with the Indians themselves. Now tell me just how you plan to get there."

So far, Columbus had talked to scholars who did not go to sea. This was his first chance to explain his scheme to a seafaring man.

Martín Pinzón was no scholar. He did not know or care whether the earth is round. But as he listened, he came to believe that Columbus could do as he said. There really was a way to reach India by sea! And the men who reached it first would make their fortunes.

"I wonder that the Portuguese haven't beaten you to it," he remarked. "They are fearless fellows, those Portuguese. You know they were the first to reach Africa. I should think this voyage to India would just suit them."

"I was afraid some Portuguese might try it," Columbus answered. "But so far they haven't done so."

"Well, they don't need the Indian trade just now," Pinzón answered. "All their ships are busy bringing cargo from the African coast. Now let's get down to business. You will need three ships. Two won't do. One might be wrecked. Then the second would have to carry a double crew and supplies. That would leave no room for cargo. Bales of silk take up a great deal of space. Gold is heavy, too. Yes, three ships it must be."

"I had thought of more," Columbus answered. "Six, perhaps."

Pinzón shook his head.

"And where would you find so many honest captains?" he asked. "No, no, my friend. I have had experience. A big fleet gets scattered too easily. We don't want some scoundrel making off with our precious goods. Three ships are just right. You will command one. I will take the second. We can surely find one good man for the third."

Columbus looked at him with sparkling eyes.

"You, Captain Pinzón?" he asked. "*You* will come with me?"

The big man laughed. "Certainly. When has Martín Pinzón refused such a chance? Do you know the price of silk today? Or of gold? And pearls—our lords and ladies can never get enough of them. Oh, yes, friend Columbus. You can't shake me off now. We will make the voyage together. It's all settled. Here's my hand on it."

Solemnly the two men shook hands. Then they began eagerly making their plans. Columbus told of the trouble he had had with the shipowners.

"Just leave that part of it to me," Pinzón

said. "I'll dazzle these fellows with promises of great wealth. They know me. They know I'm not the man to fail in what I undertake. And while I'm getting the ships, you round up the men to sail them."

"Fair enough," Columbus agreed. With a light heart he went home to La Rábida.

Pinzón was as good as his word. He talked three shipowners into renting him their ships. The largest ship was the *Santa María*. She was slow and clumsy, but stoutly built. The *Pinta* was the swiftest of the three. The *Niña*, whose name means "Little One," was the smallest and the best.

Columbus wished that he could choose the *Niña* for himself. But he was the Admiral in command of the expedition and must sail in the biggest boat. So the *Santa María* was chosen as his flagship.

One day Columbus took Diego down to the harbor to see the three ships. It was a disappointment to Columbus that his son was frightened of the sea. Thirteen-year-old Diego had never forgotten the short, unpleasant journey from Portugal to Spain.

"Yes, I suppose it's a nice ship, for a *ship*," he said when Columbus pointed out the *Santa*

María. "But oh, Papa, aren't you afraid to go away out on the Ocean Sea? What if the ship sinks? How will you ever get back?"

Two sailors were lounging near them. They caught the boy's words. One of them winked at the other. "There's a youngster with good sense," he said loudly. "The *Santa María* is supposed to be going to India. And she must cross the Ocean Sea to get there! Why, even a child knows it can't be done."

Columbus put his hand on Diego's shoulder. "Come along, son. We'll be getting back to the monastery now. Perhaps some day, when you're older, you'll feel differently about the sea. I hope so!"

CHAPTER ELEVEN

Three Ships A-Sailing

CAPTAIN PINZON looked up from his desk. "Any luck, my friend?" he asked.

"No luck," Columbus replied, wearily entering Pinzón's office. "I have spent the day on the waterfront. I have talked to dozens of sailors. Not one of them will come with us."

"What do they say?" Pinzón asked.

"They talk nonsense," Columbus answered furiously. "It's the Ocean Sea that scares them. 'What?' they say. 'Shall we go out where the sea serpents are? Where waves run mountain-high and boiling hot? Shall we take a chance of falling off the edge of the earth? Oh, no. The men of Palos are not such fools as that!' "

He dropped into a chair. Pinzón looked at him gravely.

"We have plenty of officers," he observed. "My brother and some of my friends will join us. It is only common seamen we lack."

"And common seamen we must have," Columbus answered. "But how?"

"There is a way," Pinzón said thoughtfully. "You may not like it. But it would get us the men we need."

"Then I will like it," Columbus answered. "What is this way?"

"We could take volunteers from the jails," Pinzón said. "Oh, I don't mean real criminals. But in a seafaring town like this, sailors ashore often get into trouble. Our Spanish courts are slow. The jails are crammed with men awaiting trial. They are charged with small crimes like gambling or disturbing the peace. Many of them would rather sail with us than serve a jail sentence."

"I see," Columbus answered. "Do your judges permit this?"

"Yes," Pinzón replied. "Of course, these men can't be forced to volunteer. They must agree of their own free will."

"Well, it's worth trying," Columbus said.

[107]

"Already weeks have gone by. And we have accomplished nothing."

"Oh, don't say that. We have our three ships. We have some good pilots and navigators. Courage, my friend!" Pinzón slapped Columbus on the shoulder. "Before summer comes we'll be on our way."

"I hope so." Columbus got up and turned toward the door. "I'll talk with some of the prisoners tomorrow."

He went out into the street. A crippled beggar boy sat on the steps of a church near by. His twisted foot was tucked up under him. Columbus tossed a penny into his cap and went on.

He took the long uphill road to La Rábida. Halfway up, he heard footsteps behind him. A voice called his name.

"Captain Columbus! Please, sir, one word! One minute!"

Columbus stopped. It was the beggar boy from the church steps. In spite of his crippled foot, he came quickly up the hill. He was panting as he stood before Columbus.

"Catch your breath, lad," Columbus said

kindly. "There is no hurry. Now. What is it you want with me?"

The boy hesitated. He had a merry, impudent face. But now he looked very shy. At last he spoke.

"Sir, I beg for my living. What else can I do? I am an orphan. No one would teach me a trade. But in my heart I am no beggar. This is no life for me. I am meant for better things!"

Columbus started. Long ago in Genoa another boy had spoken those very words. He had been that boy. He too had determined to change his life. His voice was very gentle as he spoke.

"And what life would you choose, my son?"

"A sailor's life!" The words tumbled out. "Oh, sir, don't laugh as the other captains do! My foot is twisted as you see. But truly, sir, it is not a bad foot. It does not keep me from standing, or walking, or running. A sailor must be able to climb, the captains say. Perhaps I could not climb so well. But there are other jobs on a ship, surely? Oh, Captain Columbus, if you will take me, if only you will take me—"

[*109*]

The pleading eyes were big in the dirty face. Columbus considered. Out of all Palos, this crippled boy was the first volunteer. He would come willingly, gladly. Well, why not?

"What is your name, and where do you live?" he asked.

"They call me Pedro, sir. I have no family and no home. I sleep in doorways or under the sky. Captain, will you take me with you?"

"I will take you," Columbus said. "When I was your age, I went to sea as a cabin boy. You shall come as mine. Do you see that ship there, the *Santa María?* It will be your home. Tell the watchman I said you were to sleep aboard tonight."

"That beautiful ship—my home?" The beggar boy suddenly sank to his knees in the dust. He caught Christopher's hands and covered them with kisses. "Oh, sir, I will serve you all my life. Never, never can I repay such kindness!"

The Spanish sailors believe that a cripple brings good luck. Perhaps this was true. For after he found Pedro, Christopher's luck changed. He recruited fifty able seamen from the jails. The Queen sent him some discharged soldiers, who had once been fishermen, and knew something of sailing.

Then some Palos sailors changed their minds and decided to join the expedition. Word of the riches in India had spread fast. After all, these men thought, it was worth taking a little risk, to come home with pockets full of pearls. Many of their wives and mothers wept and repeated the old stories of sea monsters. But little by little Columbus found all the men he needed.

[*111*]

He and Pinzón and the sailors worked hard getting the three ships ready. They stocked them with sea biscuits, dried fish, and salt meat. There were barrels and barrels of fresh water. In addition to these supplies, the ships carried all sorts of trinkets for trade.

By the night of August 2, 1492, all was ready. The last of the stores had been stowed away. The last sailor was aboard. The three ships lay in harbor, waiting for the tide. And Columbus, with his principal officers, climbed the hill to La Rábida to ask a blessing on the expedition.

They gathered in the monastery chapel. Father Pérez spoke solemnly to them. He reminded them that they were going to the East as the first Christians. All Christians everywhere would be judged by their actions. Let them see to it that they brought credit upon their Master's name.

Young Diego knelt by his father's side. He was happy because he was to remain at home among the good monks. They would keep him safe until his father's return.

The service ended. Columbus kissed his son

good-by. Diego promised to pray day and night for a safe voyage. Father Pérez asked a final blessing.

Columbus and his officers went back to Palos. Silently they tramped through the dark streets. There were no cheering crowds to see them off. In the dark houses the women of Palos wept bitterly. Their men were going off into the unknown, and they were afraid that they would never come home again.

The party separated at the docks. Small

boats rowed the officers to their ships. Martín Pinzón commanded the *Pinta*. His young

brother Vicente was captain of the little *Niña*.
Columbus stepped aboard the *Santa María*.
Just before sunrise he gave the order to sail.

The fresh morning breeze filled the snowy
new sails, marked with green crosses. Flags
fluttered up the tall mainmasts. The last line
was cast off. Slowly the leading ship moved out
to sea.

High on its hill, the monastery of La Rábida
looked down upon the harbor. An old man

and a boy stood at the wall, waving frantically. The three ships moved more quickly now, drawing away from their sight. At last Diego could see them no more.

"Papa is gone, Father Pérez," Diego said fearfully. "He's gone out into the Ocean Sea. Oh, will he ever come back?"

"He will come back, my child," Father Pérez answered serenely. "Your father is a good man, and a brave one. Have no fear for him. Our Lord will keep him safe."

CHAPTER TWELVE

On the Ocean Sea

M AY it please my lord Admiral—"

Christopher Columbus laid down his spy-glass. All afternoon he had stood, high on the forecastle, peering ahead. With a frown he looked down at the seamen who were crowding up the ladder.

"Well, well, what is it?" he asked. "Why are you not about your duties?"

The leader was a tall man with a tough, scarred face. The others shoved him forward.

"My lord Admiral," he said boldly, "we have come for a word with you. The men are sick of this endless sailing. Thirty days without sight of land! We have had enough of it. We want to put the ship about and go home."

[*117*]

"Yes, yes!" the other men shouted. "We want to go home!"

Columbus looked calmly into the angry faces.

"What is your complaint?" he asked. "We have had good weather and fair winds. You have seen for yourself that the Ocean Sea is not a place of monsters and boiling waves. This has been a good voyage so far."

"So far!" the leader echoed. "But how do we know what we will come upon tomorrow? Yes, we have been lucky. But good luck does not last forever. While we are still safe, we want to turn back."

"And if I refuse?" Columbus asked.

There was a pause. The men shuffled their feet and whispered among themselves.

The leader fingered the knife at his belt.

"It will be better if Your Grace does not refuse," he said insolently.

Columbus straightened himself. His eyes flashed, but he kept his voice to a quiet, friendly tone.

"I chose my crew for courage," he said. "Some of you came to me from the Palos jail.

I did not ask what your crimes had been. All I wanted were men who were not afraid to take a great risk for a great reward. Most of the risk is over. At any minute now we will sight the rich land of India. There your reward awaits you. Would you turn your backs on it now?"

Again the sailors whispered together. Then an old man spoke anxiously.

" 'Tis not that we are cowards, Your Grace," he said. "But the long waiting has worn us down. If we could be sure it wouldn't last much longer—"

"You can be sure," Columbus answered with confidence. "By my reckoning, we should have reached India today. We must allow for small errors in reckoning. India can be no more than a few hours away. Don't you think I am as eager to see it as you are? I promise you, it won't be long."

The leader fingered his knife again. Columbus spoke quickly.

"Suppose I listened to you," he said, "and turned the *Santa María* back? Do you think Captain Pinzón would do the same? Oh, no.

[*119*]

The men of the *Pinta* and the *Niña* would go on to scoop up the Indian pearls. Think of the talk in Palos! The brave men of two ships come home rich. But the cowards of the *Santa María* slink back with empty pockets. Is that what you want?"

"Indeed we don't want that, master," the old man quavered. "If you could just give us a word about how long it will be—"

"Very well," Columbus answered. "I'll give you a word. To be safe, I'll say three days. In three days, probably less, we will certainly reach land. This I promise you on my sacred honor!"

The scowling faces lightened. Here and there a smile broke out. The mutiny was over.

Awkwardly the men stumbled back down the ladder. Columbus returned to his charts. He had had a little table brought up here to the highest point of the ship. Carefully he went over his figures again.

Columbus was never to know how wrong those figures were. He supposed the earth to be much smaller than it really is. He knew nothing of the American continent and the

Pacific Ocean. He would have had to cross both of them to reach India. He would have had to travel thousands and thousands of miles.

It is a good thing he did not know this. He felt cheerful as he studied his maps. Yes, he

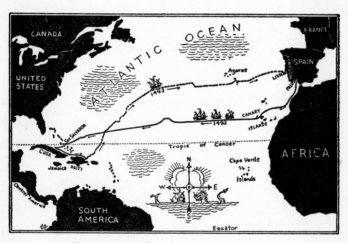

Route of Columbus's First Voyage

had been safe in promising land within three days. The figures showed it.

His cabin boy interrupted his studies.

"Your supper is getting cold in your cabin, master," he said.

Columbus looked up.

"Supper, Pedro? You may bring it here."

The boy came back with the tray of salt fish, ship's bread, and olives. He set out the food on the little map table. Then he spoke timidly.

"Master, may I show you something?"

Columbus looked surprised. It was not like Pedro to ask questions. The boy was usually silent, going about his work with anxious care. It seemed he could never do enough to show his gratitude.

Columbus had done well when he picked up the beggar boy in Palos. Pedro gave all his time to his master's comfort. Thanks to Pedro, there was always good hot food and clean dry clothing. The cabin was kept in perfect order. Never in all his days at sea had Columbus been so well cared for.

"What do you want to show me, Pedro?" he asked kindly.

"This." Pedro laid a crumpled wad of feathers on the table. He smoothed it out. It was a small dead bird.

"Is it a lark?" the boy asked shyly. "It looks like the larks we have at Palos. But I have never before seen a lark at sea."

[122]

Columbus took the bird into his hands.

"It is no lark, but certainly it is no sea bird," he said. Excitement crept into his voice. "This creature came from the land! Where did you find it, Pedro?"

"It flew into the mast, sir. I think the blow stunned it. It was living when it fell to the deck. I tried to feed it, but it died soon."

"A land bird!" Columbus rose to his feet. "Then this proves it. Land is near. Oh, Pedro, my lad, you have brought me wonderfully good news!"

"I have, sir?" Pedro's eyes shone with delight. "Oh, I am glad. Because—because I have some other news that is not good. I must tell you, master. I heard Black Juano talking to some of the others. You know Juano? With the scars on his face? He was here this afternoon."

"I know him. Go on."

"He says they were fools to believe you, master. He says we will not find land in three days, or three years. And he wants—he wants —oh, dreadful things, sir. I don't know how to tell you."

"Tell me, Pedro."

"Well, master, he says they should wait the three days. Then, if no land is found, they must act. They must seize you and make you turn back. And if you won't, Black Juano says his knife will take care of you. Oh, he is a wicked one, that Juano! They will toss your body overboard and say you fell. And—"

"Just a minute, Pedro," Columbus broke in. "I thought the men seemed satisfied when they left me. Are they all plotting against me?"

"Not all, sir. Only Juano and three others.

But that is enough. They would not stop at murder. Once you are dead, they will rule the ship. And the others do want to go home, you know."

"I know. Well, your good news outweighs your bad, Pedro. The little bird tells us land is near. We won't worry about Juano and his friends. In three days, or less, they'll come back and thank me. All their complaints will melt away when we sight land. And that may be any minute now."

Columbus picked up his spyglass again.

"Are you going to stay up here and watch, sir?" Pedro asked. "Surely the lookout man will call you when he sees anything."

"I'd rather trust my own eyes," Columbus answered. "Yes, I'll stay here for a while. You may keep me company if you like."

All that long night Columbus kept watch. Pedro crouched at his feet.

The moon came up, turning the black waters to silver. On either hand shone a glimmer of light from the other ships, the *Pinta* and the *Niña*. Perhaps their captains, Martín Pinzón

and his brother Vicente, were watching too.
Columbus watched all night, and all the
next day. He saw no land. He did see one

curious thing, however. Toward dusk of the
second day the *Pinta* crowded on full sail. She
pushed past the *Santa María* and soon was far
in front.

Columbus had given no orders for the *Pinta*
to go ahead. Captain Pinzón, it seemed, was
not waiting for orders.

Columbus smiled to himself. Pinzón was a

vain man. He would like to boast afterward that he was the first to see the Indian shore. Well, let him have that pleasure!

A light mist came up at nightfall. The *Pinta* disappeared into it. The *Santa María* plowed steadily on, favored by a fresh breeze. The little *Niña* skimmed over the waves at her side. At ten o'clock a brilliant moon rose and the mist vanished. The long night wore on.

Columbus and Pedro were alone on the forecastle. The boy was dozing when a strange sound wakened him suddenly.

"Master!" He jumped up. "What is that?"

"Quiet, boy. Listen!"

It came again, clear above the sound of wind and wave. A loud, heavy "Boom!" that could mean but one thing. The *Pinta* was firing off her little cannon. This was the signal which meant that someone on Pinzón's ship had sighted land.

The shot awakened the *Santa María's* men, sleeping on deck. They jumped up with wild shouts of "Tierra! Tierra! (Land! Land!)" They did not wait for the Admiral's orders to

[*127*]

crowd on sail. With a burst of speed the *Santa
María* shot forward.

Soon the men could see the land for themselves. A white sandy cliff glimmered in the

moonlight. Behind it was a dark line of trees.
The *Niña* and the *Santa María* came close
enough to hail the *Pinta*. Over the noise of
excited voices Columbus shouted his con-

gratulations to Pinzón. He did not rebuke him for racing him and arriving first. This sort of honor was dear to Pinzón. It meant nothing to Columbus. They had sighted land at last. That was all he cared about.

The shore before them was rimmed with coral reefs. It would never do to try to pass them. The three ships sailed along the coasts until daylight. Then they came to a sheltered little bay with a smooth sandy beach. It was a perfect harbor.

CHAPTER THIRTEEN

Can This Be India?

THE rising sun showed a crowd of men pouring out of the woods and onto the beach. Young Pedro, standing at his master's elbow, watched eagerly.

"So those are Indians," the boy exclaimed. "I never knew the people of India went naked, master. Don't they know how to make cloth?"

Columbus frowned. He was as puzzled as the boy. Marco Polo had written of the fine silk robes worn at the Oriental courts. Then an explanation came to him.

"No doubt these men are peasants," he said. "Perhaps only the nobles wear clothing. Is the longboat ready, Pedro?"

"The rowers are taking their places, master. And boats are putting out from the *Pinta* and the *Niña*. Shall I bring the flag?"

Columbus nodded. It amused him to see how Pedro was losing his shyness. He had encouraged the boy to chatter in the long night watches. Now, it seemed, there was no stopping him.

Pedro hurried off and came back with the royal banner. It was very beautiful. Queen

Isabella's ladies had made it. There was a great green cross, and the initials of Ferdinand and Isabella under gold crowns.

The Admiral took his place in the longboat. Pedro managed to squeeze in among the rowers. "I am in charge of the flag," he told a sailor who tried to stop him.

Boats from the three ships reached the beach at the same time. Martín Pinzón and his brother Vicente of the *Niña* jumped ashore.

At the Admiral's command, the flagstaff was set up in the sand. Columbus and the two captains fell on their knees. So did Pedro, and the

The Admiral gave thanks to Almighty God
for a safe arrival

men who had rowed the boats to shore.

The Admiral lifted his voice and gave thanks to Almighty God for a safe arrival. The prayer was very long. Pedro, peeping through his fingers, saw the Indians standing quietly by. They were staring at the lovely banner with its cross and golden crowns.

After the prayer was finished the Admiral made a speech. He said he was taking possession of this land in the name of Spain, and calling it San Salvador. When he ended, his men knelt before him, as they would have knelt before the King or Queen.

Then Columbus turned to the natives.

"Take me to your master, the King of India," he commanded in Spanish.

The Indians smiled and shook their heads. He tried again in Italian, in Portuguese, and in Latin. Still they could not understand him.

Martín Pinzón stepped forward.

"Let me try the sign language," he said. "I had some experience with the natives of Africa."

He tried the signs the Africans had understood. The Indians watched carefully. Then

[*135*]

they began to nod and smile. They turned and ran quickly back toward the woods.

"I have ordered them to bring their King to us," Pinzón said importantly. "It is not dignified for us to seek him out. They will bring him here."

"Good," Columbus answered. "I wonder if he will come riding on his elephant? I should like to see one of those beasts."

They waited only a little while. Then the Indians came back. They brought no king, and no elephant. Instead they carried palm-leaf trays heaped high with fruits. These they placed before the visitors. Then they all knelt down, as they had seen the white men do.

Columbus glanced at Pinzón.

"Your sign language is not much good so far, Captain," he said. "Never mind. These are simple country people. We'll hope to do better at court. The question is, how do we reach the court?"

"There may be a city behind those trees," Pinzón suggested. "Perhaps the court is there."

"If that were so," Columbus said, "the King

would surely have sent someone to find out who we are. No, this must be some remote place, far from the cities. I think we'd do well to have ourselves rowed up the coast. India must have seaports. We're bound to come upon one."

Columbus called the sailors to him.

"You men can have shore leave until sunset," he told them. "See that you treat these Indians kindly. I'll be back by nightfall. No, Pedro, you're not to come with me. Stay here and guard the flag."

The sailors spent a pleasant day on the sunny beach. They enjoyed the fresh fruit, most of it strange to them. They had never seen pineapples or bananas before. Later in the day the Indians brought them cooked yams and broiled fish.

Pedro struck up an acquaintance with an Indian boy about his own age. He was a slim brown lad with a bright, laughing face. The two boys sat in the shade of a big rock and tried to talk.

Pedro touched his own chest. "Pedro," he said. He touched his chest again and repeated

[*137*]

the word. Then he pointed his finger at the other boy.

The young Indian smiled. "Pedro," he said.

"No, no! *I* am Pedro! Who are you? Watch, now. I touch myself. Pedro, me. You?" Again he pointed.

The boy understood at last. He pounded his own chest.

"Taino," he said with a laugh.

"Oh, good! Now we know each other's names. Pedro. Taino. Say it."

To Taino this was a very funny game. He laughed delightedly as Pedro went on to other words. Foot. Sand. Sky. Soon each boy had learned these words in the other's language.

The sun sank low. The ships' officers began gathering the men to return to the ships. Pedro had to say good-by to his new friend.

The longboat carrying Columbus and Pinzón returned to the *Santa María* shortly after dark. Pedro served supper to the two men in the Admiral's cabin. He listened eagerly to their talk.

"I'm sadly disappointed," Pinzón began.

[*138*]

"We know now that this is only a small island inhabited by naked savages. It is not India."

"No, it isn't," Columbus agreed. "But it may be something just as good. It may be a part of Cipango. Marco Polo said Cipango is made up of many islands."

"Marco Polo!" Pinzón sneered. "The man who wrote of beaches strewn with pearls. Where are the pearls? Where are the silks and spices? Above all, where is the gold? Golden

[*139*]

palaces, you promised me. You were a fool to believe Marco Polo, Columbus. And I was a fool to believe you."

Pedro almost dropped the platter he was carrying. That any man should dare to speak to the master like that! What would the Admiral do? Draw his sword and run him through?

The boy held his breath. But Columbus answered calmly enough.

"You are tired, Pinzón. And disappointed, as I am myself. But we must not feel badly. We have reached the beginning of the Eastern world. From our boat today we saw other islands. There may be many before we come to the mainland. What does it matter? We have only to sail on. Sooner or later we will come to the place where the riches are."

"Well, the sooner the better," Pinzón said sourly. He finished his dinner and rose. "I'll be getting back to the *Pinta* now. How long do we stay in this dreadful place?"

"Not long," Columbus assured him. "A day or two to take on fresh water. Sleep well, Captain. The world will look brighter tomorrow."

When Pinzón had gone Pedro approached Columbus.

"Sir, I talked to one of the Indian boys to-day. His name is Taino. I think I could teach him Spanish very quickly. And already I have learned a few words in his language."

Columbus looked pleased.

"An interpreter, eh? That's exactly what we need. I'd been thinking of taking some Indians along as pilots. They seem very skillful with their dugout canoes. Your friend can come. Ask him to find four or five men who know the channels."

"Yes, sir. And I'll teach them all Spanish," Pedro said eagerly.

So, Taino and five other Indians were aboard when the *Santa María* sailed. Pedro found that teaching them Spanish was not easy. Only Taino learned quickly, and he had difficulty with his sentences. But it did not matter, for Pedro became very good in the Indian language.

The Admiral put Pedro in charge of the Indians. They did everything he told them. The sailors called them "Pedro's army."

[*141*]

It did not take long to explore the little islands near San Salvador. Then Columbus struck out for a larger island to the west. The Indians called it Cuba. According to them, it was a wonderful place, with wonderful sights to see.

The Admiral's hopes rose. Cuba must be the principal island of Cipango, where the King lived. At last, at last, he would see the wonders which Marco Polo had described!

CHAPTER FOURTEEN

The Pinta *Sails Alone*

WELL?" Martín Pinzón spoke with a sneer. "We have seen it all, this wonderful island of Cuba. It would be different from the smaller islands, your guides told us. They said the people here wear clothing and live in castles. Clothing—a twist of cotton cloth! Castles —made of grass and palm leaves! Is this what your Marco Polo called Cipango?"

Columbus settled his aching bones on the grass. For several days he and Pinzón had journeyed about the island. The Indians had carried them in hammocks slung on poles. It had been almost as tiring as walking.

They were near the beach now. Columbus could look down on the beautiful bay, where the three ships lay at anchor.

[*143*]

"Cuba is not Cipango," he admitted. "It is not a civilized country. I hoped we would find

a city when we went inland. But everywhere it is the same. Forests, grass huts. The people are gentle and friendly. They bring us gifts—"

[144]

"Yes, and what gifts!" Pinzón interrupted. "Darts tipped with sharks' teeth. Live parrots. Skeins of cotton thread. Have we taken this long voyage to bring home such trash? Where are the pearls, the silk, the gold?"

"There is gold somewhere in these isles," Columbus said. "The boy Taino showed my gold pin to these Cubans. In their own tongue he asked where he could find gold like it. They said there was plenty in another great island to the south."

"A likely story!" Pinzón snorted. "These savages tell us what we want to hear. They care nothing for the truth." But a greedy glint had come into his eyes. "Where is this other island, then?" he asked. "Does Taino know?"

"He was to find out more about it while we were away," Columbus replied. "We'll question him after dinner. Are you rested now? I see a boat waiting to take us to the *Santa María*."

In the cabin that night they heard Taino's report. With Pedro to prompt him, the Indian boy spoke in Spanish.

"Island called Haiti," he said. "More big

[*145*]

than Cuba. Big, very big! Ruled by great king, Guacanagarí. King have gold necklace, gold nose-ring. Very great king!"

"Where is this island?" Pinzón demanded. "Can the Cubans take us there?"

He spoke so quickly that Taino could not understand him. Pedro repeated the words in the Indian language.

"Not far," Taino answered. "But very rough sea between. All Cuban know the way. Don't like go there. Waves sink canoes."

"You are sure about the gold?" Pinzón insisted. "They say there really is gold in Haiti? Where do the people get it? Is there a mine?"

Again Taino was puzzled by the flood of rapid questions. He looked helplessly at Pedro.

Columbus took up the questioning. He spoke slowly in his clear, kind voice. Taino answered him easily.

Yes, there was gold in Haiti, or so the Cubans said. It came from a hole in the ground. The King's slaves dug as much as was wanted. The Haitian people didn't care much for it. They thought colored sea shells were prettier.

"Can you find a Cuban pilot to take us to Haiti?" Columbus asked.

Taino smiled. "Any fisherman can do. But much afraid. Waves sink canoe."

"They won't sink our big ships," Columbus said.

He went on with his questions. Martín Pinzón listened in silence. At last he got up to go back to his own ship.

The Indian boy looked after him and muttered something. Pedro spoke a few sharp Indian words.

"What did Taino say?" Columbus asked.

"Taino says Captain Pinzón is a bad man, master," replied Pedro. "I have scolded him for speaking so."

"That was right. You may make my bed now, Pedro. The long journey on land has tired me."

Columbus slept soundly that night. He did not see the *Pinta's* longboat go ashore. He did not see the boat return to the ship with two Cuban fishermen.

The tide turned before dawn. Silently the *Pinta* slipped out of the harbor. When day broke, there were only two ships in the bay.

Pedro brought the news with the Admiral's breakfast. When Columbus heard the news he strode out on deck and looked over the bay. It was true. The little *Niña* rode at anchor, but the *Pinta* was nowhere in sight.

Columbus sent at once for the younger Pinzón brother, captain of the *Niña*. Vicente Pinzón looked very much ashamed when he stood before the Admiral.

"I knew nothing of this, sir," he said. "My brother has complained a good deal of late. He was growing impatient to find treasure. He thinks we are wasting time here in Cuba, where there is none."

"I am beginning to think the same thing," Columbus answered. "But finding treasure is not my only duty. I am claiming all these islands for Spain. Their Majesties will expect a full report of our discoveries. I must write down an account of these new lands. Such things take time."

"I understand that, sir," Vicente said. "And I am ashamed of my brother. He should have understood it too."

"I think Martín Alonso understood very

well," Columbus said slowly. "He knew I expected to spend more time in exploring Cuba. Tell me, Captain Vicente. Did your brother speak to you of an island to the south? A place the Indians call Haiti?"

"No, sir. He never mentioned that name to me."

Columbus thought for a minute. "It was only yesterday that we heard of Haiti. The Indians say it is a great island, very rich in gold. I wonder—yes, that is it. The *Pinta* must have sailed for Haiti."

"Where the gold is, there we will find my

[*149*]

brother," Vicente said sadly. "He is mad for treasure, sir. And not treasure alone. He is mad for glory. Do you remember how he raced us to San Salvador? He was determined to be the first man to sight land. And now he will be the first man to reach Haiti and its gold."

"Well, I don't object to that," Columbus said. "If he had asked me, I would have given him permission to go to Haiti ahead of us. But he did not ask. I am in command of this expedition. To leave it without orders is desertion. Under the law, I could hang him when we catch up with him."

"Sir, you would not do that?" Vicente looked horrified.

Columbus smiled. "Hang my best captain? That would be very foolish. Your brother is greedy, and he is vain. But I've never known a man who handled a ship more skillfully. Now don't worry about him. We'll find him waiting for us on Haiti. I'll give him a stern lecture, you can be sure. He must learn that he cannot disobey his Admiral."

"Yes, sir." Young Captain Vicente sounded relieved. He was glad to talk about something else. "Do you think there really is gold on Haiti, sir?"

"The Indians say so," Columbus answered. "I must admit I am growing impatient too. I shall write my report on Cuba quickly. Get the *Niña* ready to sail tomorrow, Captain Vicente. We'll have a look at this gold island for ourselves."

The two captains had been talking on deck. Over by the rail young Pedro crouched, polishing his master's boots. He had heard every word. Now he hurried off to find Taino.

"You were right," Pedro said excitedly. "Captain Pinzón is a bad man. My poor master still doesn't think so. He hates to think ill of anyone. But it's perfectly plain to me.

"Captain Pinzón wants to find the gold on Haiti for himself. And he wants to boast that he was the first one to find it, too. His own brother says he is mad for treasure and glory. Oh, I wish he had never come with us. Or is it wrong to wish that?"

"Not wrong," Taino answered calmly. "Bad man. I tell you once. I tell you again. Bad."

"Well, I'm glad he's gone," Pedro said. "The Admiral thinks we'll find him at Haiti. I don't care if we never find him. We're better off without him."

CHAPTER FIFTEEN

Gold at Last

"MASTER, will you come to bed now?"
Pedro tugged at the Admiral's sleeve. "You
have not slept for two nights. Come and get
a good rest. There is the Christmas feast for
King Guacanagarí tomorrow. You must be
ready for it."

Columbus smiled down into the anxious
face. It was true that he was worn out.

The weather had been bad from the day
they had left Cuba. They had sailed around
Haiti, going ashore here and there. Everywhere they had battled rough seas and unfa-
vorable winds. For the last two days they had
struggled through a fearful gale.

Now, however, the winds had blown themselves out. The *Santa María* was sliding gently
over a calm sea.

"Yes, I think I can take time to rest," Columbus agreed. He called the first mate to him.

"Take the ship into the bay here," he said, pointing to the chart. "The Cubans tell me it is a safe harbor. We can't be more than an hour away from it."

"Yes, Your Grace." The first mate peered at the chart. "Will this be the royal town we've heard about, sir? Everywhere we've landed on this Haitian coast, we've heard about King Guacanagarí. I am very curious to see an Indian king."

"So am I," Columbus answered. "We'll see him tomorrow. I have invited him to Christmas dinner. Messengers took the invitation to him from our last landing place. He has sent word he will come. Well, you can take command of the ship now."

Columbus went below, and Pedro with him. Soon both were sound asleep.

The weary sailors slept too, curled up on the deck. Everyone was worn out from battling the recent storm. The mate paced the deck, yawning.

He felt that there was nothing for him to do on deck. The helmsman had only to steer by a certain star. He did not need an officer to watch him. The mate quietly left the deck and went down to his bed.

The helmsman was tired too. The Admiral and the first mate were both sleeping. They would never know if he turned over his duty to someone else. He kicked a young sailor awake.

"You take the tiller, boy," he growled. "I'll just have a little cat nap myself."

No one will ever know just what happened then. The young sailor did his best at the tiller. But some time after midnight he

[155]

ran the *Santa María* aground. She stuck fast on a coral reef, with a shuddering jar that wakened all the sleepers.

Columbus hurried on deck. All night long he worked, trying to free the ship. The *Niña,* safely at anchor, sent men to help. Nothing could be done. Christmas dawn showed that the flagship was a hopeless wreck.

With the first light, a fleet of canoes put out from the shore. The largest one was a dugout with twenty men at the oars. It reached the *Santa María* first.

A majestic figure came aboard. He was an old man, erect and dignified. His cotton mantle was studded with flat bits of beaten gold.

[*156*]

He wore gold stones in his ears, and a string of nuggets around his neck.

"It's King Guacanagarí," Pedro whispered to Taino. "Come on. The Admiral will need us to interpret."

The boys hurried forward. They translated the speech with which the King began his visit.

"It grieves me," the old man said, "that misfortune has come to my white brothers. I will do what I can to help. My men will carry your goods ashore so that nothing is lost. My house is yours. I will prepare a feast for you."

"Tell him I am grateful," Columbus said to Taino. "We had invited him to be our guest for Christmas dinner. Now, it seems, we must be his. We will be glad of his help."

The old chief unfastened his string of gold nuggets. He held it out, and spoke to Columbus. Taino interpreted his words.

"White man like this stuff," Taino said. "Messengers tell this to King. Why like? Not pretty like sea shells. More ugly than parrot feathers. But if white man like, white man keep. Guacanagarí have much more. Take!"

Columbus gladly accepted the gift. Here in Haiti he had come upon gold for the first time. Indians along the coast had traded a few ornaments with him for trinkets which he had brought from Spain. They did not have very much gold. Most of it, they said, belonged to the King. The white men would find all they wanted in the King's town.

The King's necklace was made of rough stones strung on tough grass. There had been no attempt to hammer them into shape. But they were nearly pure gold, gleaming like the sun. It was a royal gift. Columbus knew that he must find a royal one in return.

"Bring me a string of little bells," Columbus ordered Pedro. "You'll find them in the chest in my cabin."

The boy hurried off. He opened the chest filled with strings of tiny metal bells. They tinkled pleasantly as he lifted one of the strings of bells and carried it to Columbus.

The Admiral looped them around the King's neck. The old man laughed with joy at their pretty tinkling sound. Nothing could have made him happier.

[158]

At last the dugout canoes took the white men ashore for a magnificent dinner. King Guacanagarí offered them bread made from cassava root, and quantities of roast lobsters. The food was strange to Columbus and his men, but they found it very good.

They were impressed with the good manners of the Indians. The food was served on banana leaves, and there were no knives or spoons. But the Indians ate very daintily, wiping their hands on bunches of grass. Columbus noted in his report that Guacanagarí and

*King Guacanagari offered them quantities
of roast lobsters*

his court were "gentlemen, although savages."

The meal was served in the open air. When it was over, the King showed the visitors his palace. It was a very large palm-leaf hut, with no furniture but hammocks for sleeping.

"You like my house?" he asked. "My people build such houses for you. Build very quick. You sleep there tonight."

Columbus felt that the clean, airy huts which the Indians would build would be more comfortable than the poor battered *Santa María*. He gratefully accepted the King's offer. While he and his men stayed in Haiti, they lived in their new houses.

On New Year's Day Columbus had a serious talk with Vicente Pinzón.

"I have news of that rascally brother of yours," Columbus said. "I'm afraid we can't make excuses for him any longer. The Indians say a ship like ours touched at the far side of the island. It must have been the *Pinta*. As soon as I heard this, I sent your brother a letter. I told him to come to us here."

"And is he coming?" Vicente asked.

"No. That is why I say we can excuse him

no longer. The messenger says he gave my letter to the white captain. The next day the ship was gone. He has had time to join us. But as you see, he has not come."

"Did he find any gold in Haiti?" Vicente asked.

"The Indians say he traded trinkets for a few gold ornaments," Columbus answered. "But most of the gold is here, in the King's town. I can't understand his actions. He wanted gold so badly. Why doesn't he come here, where the gold is? And why doesn't he obey my orders?"

"I think I know," Vicente said sadly. "Martín Alonso is my brother. I hate to say this of him. But we must face the facts. He will not place himself under your orders again, sir. He has gone back to Spain."

"Leaving the gold behind him?" Columbus exclaimed. "He would never do that."

"I know him better than you do, sir. He will come back for the gold later. He will come back as the new governor of these islands, perhaps. For who knows what story he will tell in Spain? He will do his best to turn

Their Majesties against you. Oh, it must be so, sir. If he did not have some such scheme in mind, he would have joined us as you ordered."

"I can't believe it!" Columbus said. "He was my friend."

"A jealous friend is no friend, sir," Vicente said. "And Martín Alonso is jealous of the wealth and honors that will be yours. He wants them for himself. If he can, he will reach Spain before we do. He will have the gold ornaments to show, and a thrilling tale to tell. He—"

Columbus interrupted him with a laugh. "Now I understand. Of course, Martín Alonso must be first to get home to Spain. He must be first to tell the tale. Always first! Why didn't I remember that about him? Come now, Captain Vicente, we must not be hard on him. Let him be first as he wishes. I don't mind."

"But he will do you harm, sir," Vicente persisted.

"I think not." Columbus smiled. "The Queen is my friend. She will not listen to anyone who speaks against me. Cheer up, my friend. It will all come right. Martín Alonso may reach Spain first, but we shan't be far behind him. We are going home."

"Going home!" The words were sweet in Vicente's ears. "Yes, sir, that will be wise. But how shall we manage it? The *Niña* can never carry all the men from the *Santa María*."

"There will be no need for that," Columbus said. "We'll leave the *Santa María's* crew here. Guacanagarí will make them welcome. They can work his gold mine with picks and spades, instead of the Indians' crooked sticks. They should have a fine pile of ore ready by the time we come back.

"For we will come back!" The Admiral's voice rang out clear and strong. "Whether we have reached Cathay or Cipango I do not know. Nothing here is as Marco Polo described it. What does it matter? We have found land in the Ocean Sea. It is rich in gold. I do not think Her Majesty will be disappointed with us. I shall give her a new kingdom. And I shall return to rule it in her name."

Before nightfall Vicente had given orders to

the crew of the *Niña* to make the ship ready for the long journey home. And early one January morning the gallant little *Niña* set sail. She bore Columbus and his men safely home to Spain.

Columbus was to make three more voyages across the Atlantic and back. On one of them he would discover the vast South American continent. But his first voyage was the most important. He had dared the Ocean Sea. He had found a path to the Western Hemisphere.

Perhaps Columbus was not the first white man to cross the Atlantic. It seems likely that the Vikings reached North America long before his day. But if they did, they kept their discovery to themselves. It was Christopher Columbus who opened the way to a free, brave New World for all mankind.

CHAPTER SIXTEEN

A Dream Come True

M AKE way for my lord Don Christopher Columbus, high lord Admiral of the Ocean Sea!"

The herald's shout was followed by a fanfare of golden trumpets. Every eye turned toward the closed doors at the far end of the throne room.

Young Diego shivered with excitement.

"Will we see Papa now, Father Pérez?" he whispered.

The good priest smiled down at the boy. On Diego's other side, Uncle Bartholomew squeezed his hand. They were all here, the people Christopher Columbus loved best. The Queen herself had sent for them. This was to be truly a royal welcome.

Slowly the doors swung open. A gasp went up from the lords and ladies. Even Their Majesties looked startled.

Leading the way, came "Pedro's army," Taino and the five other Indians. Pedro limped ahead, very smart in the new doublet and hose the Admiral had given him. His face was shining with pride.

The Indians were dressed in cotton loincloths. Their copper bodies were painted in green and yellow designs. Strands of sea shells hung about their necks and wrists and ankles. On their heads were high crowns of bright-hued parrot feathers.

Pedro marched them smartly up to the throne. Then he nodded to Taino. The Indian boy gave a signal. All the Indians dropped to their knees.

Now came the sailors from the *Niña*. They carried gold ornaments, parrots in cages, and Indian weapons. One man had an armful of knotted-string hammocks. Another had a calabash full of gold dust. Several carried string bags of golden nuggets.

The sailors laid their offerings before the

throne, and knelt in their turn. There was a hushed silence. Then the Indians and sailors rose. Quietly they stepped to either side. A path between them was left for the Admiral.

Here he came at last, walking with Vicente Pinzón. Christopher's hair was gray now. Hardship and worry had carved deep lines in his thoughtful face. But he carried his head high, striding proudly to the foot of the throne. There he knelt and gallantly lifted the Queen's hand to his lips.

"It's Papa!" Diego's joyful shout broke the silence. Queen Isabella looked toward the boy and smiled. Then she drew Columbus to his feet. She spoke to a servant.

"A chair for the Admiral. Place it here, between the thrones. Now sit, my lord Admiral. You have much to tell us."

Diego stirred restlessly. Uncle Bartholomew bent down to him.

"Patience a little longer, nephew. When Their Majesties have heard him, your father will come to us."

The words reached Pedro, now squatting with his Indians on the floor. He reached up and beckoned to Diego. The boy slid down beside him.

"Is the Admiral your father?" Pedro whispered. "Then you must be Diego. He often spoke of you."

"You were with him, weren't you?" Diego whispered back. "Tell me about these savages. Do they eat people?"

Pedro chuckled. "Do you hear that, Taino? The Admiral's son wants to know if you eat people."

"No," Taino answered seriously. "We eat fish. We eat banana. Why we eat people? Foolish talk."

Diego stared. This painted heathen could understand Spanish. And speak it too, although not well. How could that be?

He had a hundred questions to ask. But when he looked up, he saw Uncle Bartholomew's frown. "Hush!" his uncle whispered. "Listen to what Papa is saying."

Columbus was speaking of what should be done with the new land.

"In my opinion, Your Majesties, it will be well to establish colonies there. These Indians know nothing about mining gold. But they are good workers. They would soon learn. Send them good masters, who will teach them to mine and to farm. We saw fine farming land there. New Spain could raise grapes and olives to ship to you here at home.

"Also, strange plants grow there which make good food. I have brought some specimens. The banana and pineapple are very tasty fruits. There is a grain called maize which we could feed to cattle. And cotton grows in abundance. Oh, it is a rich land, Your Majesties! And not all the riches are in gold."

He talked on and on. The Queen seemed never to tire of listening, and of asking questions.

The crowd in the hall waited impatiently. They were anxious to look at all the queer things which the sailors had brought. But no

[*171*]

one dared to move or speak until the royal couple gave the word.

Perhaps King Ferdinand was as curious as his nobles. He fidgeted on his throne and peered down at a caged parrot. His Majesty supposed it was a pigeon. But who ever saw a green pigeon with red wings and a yellow head?

The Queen and Columbus were talking now about teaching the Indians to become Christians. Columbus said that when he returned to New Spain he would take along several missionary priests. There was plenty of stone in the islands. The Indians could be put to work building churches. All they needed was someone to direct them.

The parrot which the King was watching gave a sudden squawk. Then it shouted some angry words. King Ferdinand could not believe his ears. The creature seemed to be saying "Shut up, shut up!" And saying it in Spanish!

One of the sailors jumped. He had spent many hours on the long voyage home teaching the bird to say those words. But he certainly had not intended them to be spoken at court.

His Majesty could wait no longer to see the things which Columbus had brought home. He broke into the conversation between the Admiral and the Queen.

"My dear, we shall have the Admiral with us at dinner," he said. "There will be plenty of time to talk then. At the moment, it pleases us to examine these strange gifts he has brought."

Queen Isabella was a dutiful wife. "I beg your pardon, my lord," she said at once. "Let us look at the presents, by all means."

The crowd swarmed around the sailors and the Indians. Columbus made his way to where the two boys stood. He gathered Diego in a warm embrace. Then he greeted Father Pérez and his brother.

"Will you have new maps for me to make, Christopher?" Bartholomew asked presently.

"Dozens of them, brother! I've drawn some rough sketches, but I haven't your skill. Why don't you come with me on my next voyage? Then you can make good maps on the spot."

"I never cared much for sailing," Bartholo-

[*173*]

mew reminded him. "But I'd like very much to see these new lands. Yes, perhaps I'll go along next time."

"And you, Diego?" Columbus smiled at his son. "You're as old as Pedro here. Shall we take you with us when we go back to Haiti?"

Diego looked unhappy. It was wonderful to have a father who went bravely into savage places. But to do it himself—oh, that was different! He looked appealingly at Father Pérez.

"Her Majesty has another plan for Diego," the priest said. "She wants him to live here at court, as page to the little prince. Diego thinks he would like that."

[*174*]

"Well, a boy should please himself," Columbus said. "Those were my father's words, a long time ago. Dear old Father—how sad that he did not live to see this day!"

"He would be proud of you," Bartholomew said. "I think Her Majesty wants you, Christopher."

Columbus hurried to his Queen's side.

"We are going into the royal chapel," she told him. "I have ordered a special Te Deum service of thanksgiving for your safe return. I regret that Archbishop Talavera is ill and cannot be with us."

Columbus smiled to himself. He remembered how Talavera had opposed his plan. The Archbishop would not want to celebrate its success. His illness was very convenient.

Illness was keeping someone else away, too. Martín Pinzón had succeeded in reaching Spain before Columbus. He had sent word to the Queen that he was ready to give her news of the New World.

Isabella had answered him with a curt letter. In it she said she would wait to hear the news from the Admiral himself. Since then,

[175]

There he knelt and gallantly

lifted the Queen's hand to his lips

Pinzón's poor health had kept him in Palos.

Quickly the brilliant procession formed for the chapel service. The Indians could not join it, for they were not yet Christians. They were sent off to lodgings in the palace yard. The sailors smoothed their hair for church. The lords and ladies found partners for the grand march into the palace chapel.

The Queen motioned to Father Pérez. "Reverend Father," she said, "will you lead the way with His Majesty? We will follow."

She waited to see that Vicente Pinzón and Bartholomew were in line together. Then,

[*178*]

with her long train trailing behind her, she swept to her place. With a smile she beckoned to Columbus.

"Walk with me, my lord Admiral!" she said.

Long ago, in Genoa, a weaver's boy had dreamed a dream. "I shall be a noble knight when I grow up! Yes, and a sea captain too!"

The proud nobles of Spain stood respectfully aside to let him pass. The Queen's jeweled hand rested lightly on his arm. At her side, Don Christopher Columbus entered the chapel. At her side he knelt, Admiral of the Ocean Sea and Governor of the Indies.

His dream had come true.

"Names That Made History"

ENID LaMONTE MEADOWCROFT, *Supervising Editor*

1 Born in Genoa, Italy, probably October 31, 1451

2 Leaves home to become a sailor, 14[

3 Gains the consent of Queen Isabella of Spain to make the first westward voyage across the Atlantic Ocean, 1492

4 Starts off from Palos, Spai[on August 3, 1492

CHRISTOPHER COLUMBUS
1451 – 1506

10 Dies at Valladolid, Spain, May 20, 1506

TRINIDAD 1498

SOUTH AMERICA

8 Reaches South Americ[on his third voyage, 1498-1500

9 Makes his fourth and last trip to the New World, 1502-1504